To the ~~██████████████████████~~ L!

Susi Feulgen

June 1950

H? Lund

Cell Growth
AND
Cell Function

Cell Growth

AND

Cell Function

A CYTOCHEMICAL STUDY

By TORBJOERN O. CASPERSSON, M.D.

Professor of Cell Research and Genetics at the Medical Nobel
Institute of the Karolinska Institute, Stockholm, Sweden

NEW YORK

W · W · NORTON & COMPANY · INC ·

PRINTED IN THE UNITED STATES OF AMERICA
FOR THE PUBLISHERS BY THE VAIL-BALLOU PRESS, INC.

TO
EINAR HAMMARSTEN

Contents

8   Contents

Cell Growth
AND
Cell Function

CHAPTER I

Introduction

EVERY DAY new opportunities are being discovered for the application of biochemistry and biophysics in general biology and the medical sciences. Biochemical and biophysical methods and interpretations stimulate biological and medical research and continually open new fields. This development necessitates, now more than ever, extensive collaboration and exchange of thought between representatives of different lines of research. On the other hand, the increasing complexity of technical procedures compels us to develop special organizations or institutions for certain types of work. The Institute for Cell Research at Karolinska Institute in Stockholm is intended as such an organization, specialized along biophysical lines.

The Institute has developed in the last decade around methods and procedures that may be applied to a *quantitative study of the chemical background of vital processes*. The work was begun in the early thirties under the stimulus of Einar Hammarsten's work on the biochemistry of nucleic acids at the Karolinska Institute. Pure basic research has been the keynote for all work done since that beginning. Methods were developed for the determination of the chemical composition of individual cell structures in order to study the chemistry of intracellular metabolism. Protein metabolism, a basic process for all growth and reproduction, has received the most attention.

A number of observations have been applied to various problems of medical interest. Such work has been planned so that it could give additional information of importance to the central basic research. Whenever possible, a specialist on the biological material in question has worked in the institution along with the resident group of research workers who are especially experienced in the technical procedures involved.

The lectures now published in book form were given in 1948 under the auspices of the Salmon Committee. I wish to take this opportunity to express my deepest thanks and appreciation to the Salmon Committee for the invitation to present this work.

The aim of these lectures and thus of this book is to give a general survey of the quantitative cytochemical work in our Institute which has led to our conception of the rôles of certain organelles in the synthesis of cellular protein and also to different working hypotheses based thereon, which might eventually serve as bases for further discussion and work. *Thus the presentation is confined to the special methods used in the Institute and to the types of biological material preferably used there.*

Even with these restrictions only basic experimental work can be covered within the space allotted. For details and also for a broader discussion in other papers, reference is made to the publications from the Institute collected in the Bibliography. The references in the text are arranged so as to indicate the various publications in which the problem in question is treated and where detailed information and references to other literature may be found. Survey articles are found in: 1936, 3; 1940, 3; 1941, 2; 1947, 1.

For the work on protein and nucleic-acid metabolism of the individual cell, microspectrographic procedures, preferably in the ultraviolet, have been used. Because of the importance of these methods for biological work carried through here, the general arrangement of the material to be presented is as follows:

Chapters II, III.—Survey of the conditions for microspectrophotometric measurements in biological materials, plan of the instrumental equipment used and discussion of the interpretation of measured data.

Chapters IV, V.—The organization of the system for protein formation in the normal metazoan cell.

Chapters VI, VII.—The organization of that system for protein formation in various pathological conditions.

Chapter VII.—The organization of that system for protein formation in lower animals and plants.

CHAPTER II

Microspectrophotometry of biological specimens (especially in ultraviolet)

THE CENTRAL problem has been to study protein metabolism since it is the primary metabolic process of growth, reproduction, and cell function.

Excluding water, the proteins are the chief constituents of living materials, and all vital processes are directly or indirectly concerned with protein metabolic processes. We know from the brilliant work of the Schoenheimer group and its successors that in an adult animal containing a *fixed* amount of protein material, the proteins are in a continuous state of breakdown and reformation.

The studies I present describe processes in individual cells, leading to synthesis of *new* protein groups in body cells, and also in the adult stage. These processes are accompanied by conspicuous fluctuations in certain cell organelles, and one of the main tasks has been to investigate the rôle played by them in metabolic processes. For this it was necessary to develop special quantitative cytochemical procedures.

1. THE TECHNICAL PROBLEM

The average diameter of the metazoan cell is around 10μ and that of many individual organelles is about 1μ or less. We must therefore be able to determine amounts of different substances down to 10^{-6} to 10^{-12} mg. It is furthermore necessary to know exactly *where* in the cell the determination is done. One should be able to determine the size, the place, and the shape of the object investigated in each case.

Optical procedures seemed from the very beginning to offer the most promising ways to meet these conditions. The most successful procedures have been based on optical principles and have been used when the light absorption of different substances could be used for their determination. Figure 1 shows the absorption over a large part of the electromagnetic spectrum by a model substance, representing a 5μ section of an average biological tissue. The figure indicates that, in different parts of the spectrum, the quantitatively most important biological substances exhibit quite different absorptions—in the concentrations and in the thicknesses of layers encountered in cytological work. In the X-ray region there are, for example, absorptions characteristic for different elements. The region between the X-rays and the ultraviolet proper is as yet accessible only with difficulty. For several future problems, however, it looks most promising. In the long-wave ultraviolet region there are absorptions characteristic for different atomic configurations within molecules. In the visible region of the spectrum the absorptions are conditioned chiefly by different molecular arrangements of cellular substances. The absorption of the individual living cell is, however, usually minimal in this spectral range. In the infrared region the main absorptions are conditioned by intermolecular and intramolecular configurations. All these spectral regions look promising for attacks on cytochemical problems. The infrared, visible, ultraviolet, and parts of the X-ray spectrum should be mentioned as technically the most easily accessible. For the study of the chemistry of the cell nucleus and of protein metabolism referred to here, practically all the technical work as yet has been done in the long-wave ultraviolet and in the visible region (1936, 1, 2, 3; 1937, 1, 2, 3, 4; 1940, 1, 2, 3; 1941, 2).

To use absorption of light in the optical region for the qualitative and quantitative chemical analyses of cellular elements, procedures of spectrophotometry and microscopy must be combined (1936, 1, 2, 3; 1937, 1–4; 1940, 1).

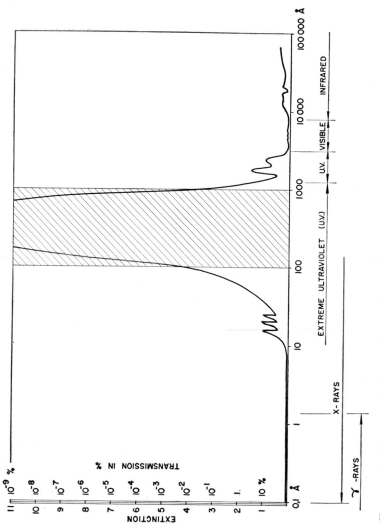

FIGURE 1. Diagram of absorptions in biological material suitable for cytochemical work.

The basic process in quantitative spectrophotometry is the measurement of the amount of light transmitted by a substance at different wave lengths (Figure 2, A and B). If the absorption spectra of several substances is known, it is possible to measure the amount of each present in a picture by analysis of the compound absorption spectrum (Figure 2 C). The shape of an absorption curve is often typical for a substance so that a *qualitative* analysis is usually possible. The height of an absorption curve is a measure of the amount of absorbing substance present, that is, it gives a *quantitative* determination.

In principle, this process could be adapted to a microscope as demonstrated in Figure 3. Then on the photographic plate one could measure the intensity of light corresponding to that transmitted by a special part of the object (1936, 1). Another method (Figure 4) is to measure the transmitted light energy with a photoelectric cell, photomultiplier tube or photoelement (1937, 4; 1940, 1, 3). If either of these procedures is repeated at a number of wave lengths, one obtains an absorption curve for the small area in question. By analysis of that curve the composition of the corresponding part with regard to light-absorbing substances can be determined (1936, 1; 1940, 1, 3).

These principles are very simple. Technical problems involved in making such measurements present a number of difficulties, however, which might easily explain the fact that no measurements of this kind had been done before on objects small enough to be of interest for fundamental biological problems. Absorption spectra in long-wave ultraviolet were taken earlier by Vlés (*Arch. Phys. Biol. 5*, 1926; *11*, 1934) on whole sea urchin eggs through a microscope system. However, since he used very low magnification and his arrangements corresponded to those used in spectrophotometry on a macroscale, his work has no technical bearing on the problems in which we are interested.

The measurement of the light-absorption curve of a very small part of a microscopical preparation appears difficult because of the complicated optical conditions in the object as well as in the com-

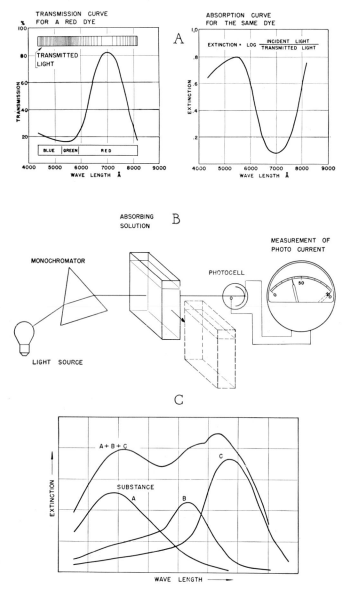

FIGURE 2. The principle of spectrophotometry: A, Transmission and absorption (extinction) curves. B, Diagram of procedure. C, Analysis of compound extinction curve by rule of three.

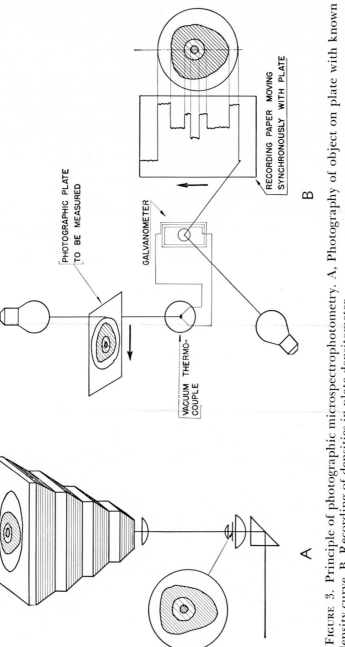

FIGURE 3. Principle of photographic microspectrophotometry. A, Photography of object on plate with known density curve. B, Recording of densities in plate densitometer.

pound microscope, which may introduce errors into the measurements.

2. THEORETICAL BASES FOR A QUANTITATIVE MICROSPECTROPHOTOMETRIC PROCEDURE (1936, 1; 1940, 3; 1947, 1; 1932, 2; 1933, 1, 2)

The theory for the formation of the image in the compound microscope is as yet not so complete that the conditions for quantitative microspectrophotometry can be calculated in every detail. *The general question can, however, be broken up into partial problems, which can be treated individually; and, especially with the aid of theoretical treatment of light dispersion in colloid solution, it can be shown that in principle it is possible to attain such a measurement with appreciable accuracy and that under certain conditions this measurement may even be simple to attain.*

The most important questions that must be answered before one can estimate the feasibility of absorption measurements of a quantitative character in the optical system of a microscope are the following (1936, 1):

To what extent does the shape of the image given by a microscope lens correspond to the true shape of the object, and to what extent does the distribution of light energy in the image correspond to the true distribution of light energy in a plane immediately behind the object?

These questions are the basic questions for all microspectrophotometric measurements. A complete agreement between the shapes and the energy distributions of image and object is the first condition for any quantitative absorption work with optical systems. A feeling that image and object do not correspond in these respects is probably the reason why real microspectrophotometric methods have been used so little. One source of this feeling might be, I believe, the well-known thesis that the microscope image can be looked upon as being composed of two images lying over each other: an "absorption image" and a "refraction image." Superficially, it seems as if the refraction image would disturb the absorption image so that an absorption measurement would give false

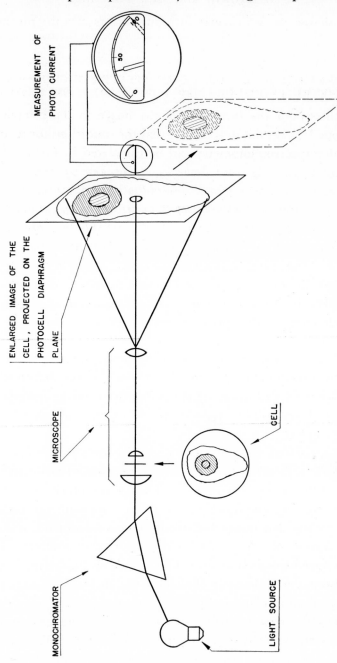

FIGURE 4. Principle of photoelectric microspectrophotometry.

values. This thesis derives from Abbe himself, but served, however, in his notable series of studies on the optics of the microscope,
merely to illustrate certain conditions in the image formation by
high aperture lenses and has no deeper physical meaning.

I will not enter into details on optical techniques but will try to
present the principle of the method we chose for studying the question of the similarity between object and image and to present the
data as a series of examples.

A. IMAGE DEFINITION AND RESOLVING POWER (1936, 1, 3)

Abbe's theory for image formation in a microscope was a monu-
mental piece of mathematical optics, but unfortunately was never
completed. Certain conditions, important for the questions at hand,
can, however, be derived from Abbe's studies. They can be briefly
presented as follows:

Behind each microscope object a diffraction spectrum appears,
which can be observed in the upper focal plane of the microscope
lens. In Figure 5, the simplest imaginable object is chosen, a rod
grating. Behind it appears a series of light spots, separated by darker
fields. The former are called spectra of the order 0, I, II, etc. Abbe
showed that the condition under which a microscope system (represented by its two principal planes, PP) will give a correct image
of such an object, that is, will show two separate images of two parallel rods, was that the main part of the light, diffracted by the
object, should enter the microscope lens. The quality and character
of the image is determined by the number of maxima entering into
the objective and participating in the formation of the definite
image, as demonstrated in Figure 5. When all light diffracted by the
object enters the lens, the definition of the image will be complete
and the intensity distribution in the image will correspond exactly
to that of the object plane. When only maximum 0 enters, the intensity distribution is entirely erroneous. All transitory stages exist.

This survey shows that for all absorption measurements, in order
to get the proper intensity distribution in the image, it is necessary
to use a lens with an aperture large enough to give full resolution

of the object to be measured in the wave length used. That condition means, in most cases, that one should not try to measure absorptions of structures smaller than three times the wave length. For details, reference is made to 1936, 1.

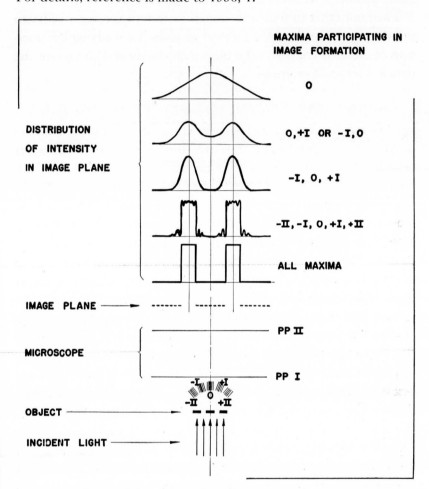

FIGURE 5. The resolving power of a microscope lens; intensity relations between object and image at different apertures.

B. THE INTENSITY RELATIONS IN OBJECT AND IMAGE (1936, 1, 3)

The second question was the relation between the distribution of light energy in the image and in the object, more exactly in a plane immediately behind the object, and is closely related to the factor presented in the previous paragraph. This relation is conditioned, on the one hand, by the properties of the optics used and on the other hand, by the properties of the object itself.

The requirements which the *image-forming optics* have to fulfill *in this respect* are, firstly, the sine condition of Abbe; secondly, that each individual point in the object is illuminated with incoherent light (1936, 1). The second condition is most easily fulfilled by arranging the illumination of the object by the principle of Köhler.

The influence of the optical properties of the *object* on the intensity relation is more complicated (for details *see* 1936, 1).

It is a well-known fact that the living cell in visible light is almost optically empty. Physically that means that the absorptions are small and the differences in refractive indices in different parts do not exceed a few hundredths of a unit. In fixed materials, however, the differences are much larger and can exceed 0.1. Experiments show that the same differences are still larger in the ultraviolet. Another factor to which attention should be drawn is that in the living but not in the fixed cell one often finds continuous changes in refractive index between intracellular phases of different optical density. I will not enter into that here and will also pass over the rare cases in which disturbances due to anomalous dispersion occur (1936, 1; 1940, 1, 2).

The influences of the optical inhomogeneities in the object are best treated as two different cases: (1) objects which are large, compared with the wave length of the light, and (2) objects which are small, compared with the wave length of the light.

Objects, large compared with the wave length of the light (1936, 1; 1932, 2)

For the presentation of this question a sphere with index of refraction, n, suspended in a medium with refractive index, n^1, may be chosen as type object. In the curves in Figures 6 and 7 the intensities are plotted as they would appear if the measurements were made on the different places of the image of the particle by an entirely ideal optical system, receiving all light deviated from the sphere (for details *see* 1936, 1, page 57). If all the light energy which has passed the object is passed on to the image, the energy distribution will correspond to Figure 6. The upper part of the figure shows

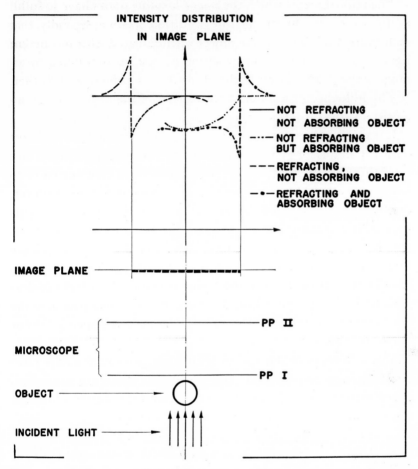

FIGURE 6. Influence of light refraction in object on intensity distribution in image plane.

how the intensity distribution in the image plane is influenced by the optical conditions in the object. The dotted curve gives the intensity distribution of a nonabsorbing object with refractive index 1.1. The curve deviates appreciably from what would be expected if the sphere did not refract the light (nonrefracting, non-absorbing object), and in intensity measurements in the image, which do not regard the refraction, a "false" absorption appears. Figure 7 presents detailed calculations on some different cases (for details *see* 1936, 1, page 61). Curves 3, 5, and 7 demonstrate the intensity distribution in the object plane when the object only absorbs and does not refract the light. The curves 2, 4, and 6 present different cases of a sphere which both refracts and absorbs the light,

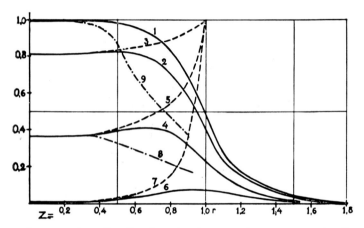

FIGURE 7. Intensity distribution in image plane, light distribution curves as in upper part of Figure 6. Numbers explained in text.

and they can be compared with the curves 3, 5, and 7 which show the absorption of a nonrefracting sphere with the same absorption coefficients. The refractive index 1.1 is, however, a very high number. It is rarely found in biological material in suitable imbedding media. It corresponds approximately to glass to water. Glass to glycerine corresponds to only a couple of hundredths in refractive index difference. Curves 8 and 9 show the course of the intensity distribution curve at a refractive index 1.5, a very high value, which probably never will occur in practical biological measurements.

From these curves and the corresponding data, it can be seen that if one limits the size of the measured field in a refracting sphere to an area close to the center of the sphere, one will get the same results in the absorption measurements as though the object had not been refracting. For the abnormally high value 1.5, it would be possible to get directly a value of the true absorption, correct to 5 per cent, if the measurement is made in an area with radius $\frac{1}{5}$ that of the sphere. With the refractive index 1.01, however, the measurement can be made in an area with a radius about 0.9 that of the sphere. If the illumination is made with convergent light, these conditions are somewhat improved.

The examples given above show that if one uses an image-forming optics that can collect all light refracted by the object, and also if the fields for the measurement are limited with regard to the refraction, it is possible to get true absorption data even in materials where index differences occur up to about $\frac{1}{10}$ of a unit of n.

Objects, small compared with the wave length of light (1936, 1; 1932, 2; 1933, 1)

A new question arises when we want to measure the absorption of particles so small that their size can be compared with the wave length of the light. The geometrical optics used above cannot be used for very small particles. The problem can, however, conveniently be treated by approximations in the following way. We can measure correctly in the microscope the absorption of particles of such a size that the loss of light can be calculated from the geometrical optics (see above). For smaller particles, however, light scattering becomes so prominent that the evaluation of the data will be increasingly difficult. Thus for practical purposes the absorption measurements should be limited to the range of dimensions where the geometrical optics is applicable.

The most convenient way to calculate this limit for the absorption measurement is to determine the size of the smallest particle for which the laws of the geometrical optics are still applicable within a predetermined limit of error. For that the theoretical work done on light scattering in colloidal solutions can be used. The optics of colloidal solutions, especially of metals, have been studied by various workers, the most comprehensive theory having been developed by Gustaf Mie. The problems within biological micro-spectrophotometry are almost entirely covered by the case of the "white sols," that is, of light-refracting and not light-absorbing particles suspended in a transparent medium. The light scattering for such solutions, with special regard to the dimensions occurring in the biological work, has been calculated from the general theory of Mie by the author (1932, 2; 1933, 1, 2). The absorption coefficients in all biological material where measurements are technically possible are so small that they do not appreciably change the shape of a light-distribution curve which makes the case of the white sols suitable for our purpose. Tables and curves have been calculated, from which the light distribution around a spherical particle of any size and any radius and at any wave length can be calculated for particle sizes occurring in the work with biological material. In the same way, the absorption curves for suspensions of a large number of such particles can be calculated from corresponding tables and curves (1932, 2, page 153 ff.; 1933, 1, page 163 ff.).

Figures 8 and 9 show sample distribution curves calculated for a series of particles of different sizes (for details *see* 1933, 1). They show, in general, that with increasing particle diameter the distribution of energy changes from the Rayleigh type of scattering to the distribution calculated according to geometrical optics. The latter appears as a special case for objects which are infinitely large, compared with the wave length of the light. For particles of the size about three times the wave length of the light used, the energy distribution, calculated by aid of the exact theory of Mie, resembles so closely the one calculated by the geometrical optics that the latter can be used for the evolution of the absorption measurements in the way mentioned above. In this case the error in the calculation of extinction coefficient, caused by the deviations from the geometrical optics, will be below 5 per cent. This corresponds to particle D on the diagram.

It is interesting to observe that the lower size limit for the measurement of absorption, given by this analysis, closely approaches the lower limit, conditioned by the properties of the microscope lenses, calculated above.

In summary these calculations show that it is theoretically possible to measure the absorption of light by particles larger than a certain minimum size $(\frac{3\lambda}{n})$, provided one takes certain precautions. They are, firstly, that one must use a lens fulfilling the sine condition

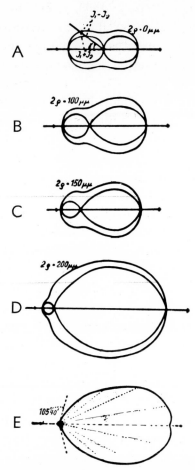

FIGURE 8. Light distribution curves around particles of different sizes. Wave length 5250 Å. Refractive index in A to D 1.18, in E 1.33. Particle diameter in A infinitely small, in B $100\mu\mu$, in C $150\mu\mu$, in D $200\mu\mu$, and in E infinitely large.

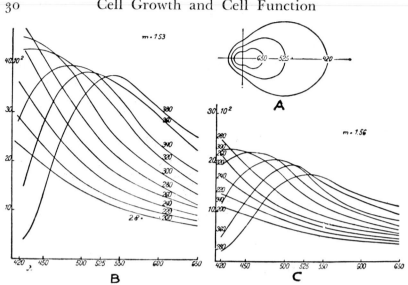

FIGURE 9. A, Light distribution curves at different wave lengths. B and C, Absorption spectra of suspensions of spheres of *nonabsorbing material*. n = refractive index sphere versus medium; diameters in millimicrons.

of Abbe; secondly, that its aperture is so large that practically all light scattered and refracted by the object enters it, and thirdly, that the measurement must be made with due regard to the refraction around the edges of the object.

That minimal size can theoretically be still lowered, if the corresponding corrections are made. These can be calculated only with a complete knowledge of the structure of the object, a factor which with further decreasing size gains importance at a rapidly increasing rate. In biological objects it is rarely possible to get such detailed data on the optical structure of specimens of the size in question.

3. TECHNICAL REALIZATION OF MICROSPECTROPHOTOMETRY TO THE THEORETICAL LIMIT IN OBJECT SIZE (1936, 1; 1940, 1)

Technically the easiest microspectrophotometric procedure would be the photographic one indicated in Figure 3. The object is photographed on a plate, the standard density curve of which is known, under the same conditions with regard to exposure and development. In large-scale work where the error must not be greater than 5 per cent the most convenient way is to standardize the exposure conditions. This can be done by calibrating the plate with respect to a standardized density curve supplied by photographing an absorbing reference system with a great number of steps, preferably a wedge, onto the plate after the object has been measured (for details *see* 1936, 1, page 71). This could be combined in one operation, for instance with a rotating sector photographed at the same time as the object; but in ultraviolet, especially below 3000 Å., such an arrangement is not profitable since the presently available optics does not allow precision work in that way, because of the inhomogeneities in the illumination of the field of vision and also because in the average biological specimen only seldom are large adjacent object-free spaces present.

Experience showed, however, from the very beginning that no photographic procedure can give the accuracy needed for real quantitative work on the *protein* content of intracellular structures. In order to analyze the absorption curves with the necessary degree of accuracy, and, at the same time, to make corrections for light refraction, it was necessary to seek for more precise methods. The accuracy in the measurement of transmission must be about 1 per cent and with a photographic procedure one cannot do better than 5 per cent without very special and time-consuming refinements. Another disadvantage with the photographic procedure is the necessity of having a comparatively large, *evenly illuminated* area, which in the ultraviolet region is very difficult to realize for a sufficiently large number of wave lengths.

Experience with the first photographic procedures in the ultraviolet showed very soon that, for an efficient attack on the problem of protein metabolism of the nucleus, it would be necessary to have equipment which fulfilled the following requirements (reasons for these conditions are given in Chapter II, paragraph 6):

(1) It must be possible to measure in a practically *continuous* spectrum down to about 2500 Å.

(2) Absorptions should be measurable in *areas as small as 0.1 square micron,* and preferably below.

(3) The *accuracy* of the transmission measurement should be *about 1 per cent,* and in special cases still higher. *With lower accuracy it is only very rarely possible to resolve a compound absorption curve of nucleic acids and protein.*

(4) It must be possible to keep the *flow of energy through the object very low,* especially in the wave-length range below 3000 Å.

As these conditions could not be fulfilled by photographic procedures, a photoelectric arrangement for absorption measurement was developed (1940, 1, 3, 4; 1937, 3, 4). Figures 10, 11, and 12 show diagrams of this arrangement.

This arrangement fulfills the first three requirements just mentioned above. With regard to (4), the measurements are arranged so that the flow of light through the preparation is just above the lowest energy level that is permitted by the statistical variations in the photoelectric currents measured. The wave lengths in which measurements are possible extend in continuous spectrum from the infrared (in this instrument 30,000 Å.) down to 2540 Å. and then in individual wave lengths down to at present about 2000 Å.

Technical data on the equipment used in ultraviolet.—The source of light for the region down to about 2500 Å. is a super high-pressure capillary mercury lamp of Philip's design, run under different conditions for different wave-length ranges. The light is dispersed in a reflecting monochromator and focused on the object with the aid of a special condenser system. Below 2500 Å. a rotating spark gap is used. The object holder can be moved by two separate arrangements. The first of these makes possible movement in any direction up to 10 mm. reproducible with an accuracy of about one micron. With the other arrangement (*see* Figure 13), the object can be moved about 20μ with a reproducibility greater than $\frac{1}{20}\mu$. This great reproducibility of movement is necessary for any measurement in different wave lengths on a small object and is one of the fundamental factors for precision measurement. The image-forming optical system is arranged behind the object holder. Any suitable optical system can be used. In ultraviolet light, the lenses worked out by Köhler and von Rohr are satisfactory for measurements from 2020 Å. to 3300 Å. In the range of 3300 Å. to 10,000 Å., Zeiss apochromates are used, equipped when needed with special correction lenses for the ultraviolet or the infrared.

In order to correct for instabilities in the light source, a part of the incident light is deflected by a thin piece of quartz and used as a standard against which the light transmitted by the specimen is balanced. This standard ray is passed through a rotating sector that may be adjusted (accurately to $\frac{1}{40}$ per cent) and read while in motion. The two light rays, one passing through the object and the other from the standard, are received by two specially built highly insulated quartz photocells, sensitive to the light being used and with identical sensitivity curves. In ultraviolet light a sodium surface is used for the region 2400–3300 Å. For longer wave lengths potassium is used and for shorter cadmium. In the visible and short infrared, potassium or compound caesium surfaces are most suitable. If lower accuracy is permissible, photomultiplier tubes are more convenient down to 3000 Å. (Philip's or RCA). If cooled to –60 degrees the RCA cells can conveniently be used to 2500 Å. and below that in combination with fluorescent materials. For precision work and work with sensitive material, the high-insulation sodium cells give considerably better performance between 2500 and 3000 Å., the region of main interest for protein metabolism.

It is necessary to keep irradiation of the object as small as possible. Furthermore, it is difficult to get enough light energy for measurement in the spectral region below 2700 Å. The optical system is arranged so that only the small central part of the field of vision of the microscope system is filled with light. The point to be measured in the object is put in the exact optical axis of the image-forming system. This axis is then projected very accurately into the center of one of the photocells. The absorption is determined by comparing the flow of energy through the object point with the flow through a part of the preparation not containing any absorbing

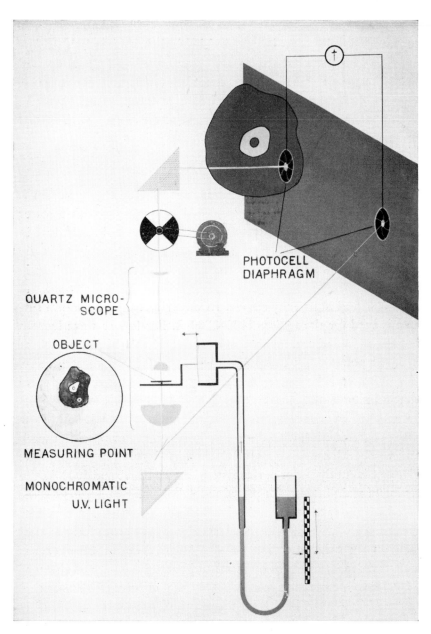

PHOTOCELL
DIAPHRAGM

QUARTZ MICRO-
SCOPE

OBJECT

MEASURING POINT

MONOCHROMATIC
U.V. LIGHT

A

FIGURE 10. Diagram of working procedure in the instrument for photoelectric microspectrography in the range 2000 Å. to 10,000 Å. A, Object to be measured projected onto photocell, rotating sector open, electric circuit in balance.

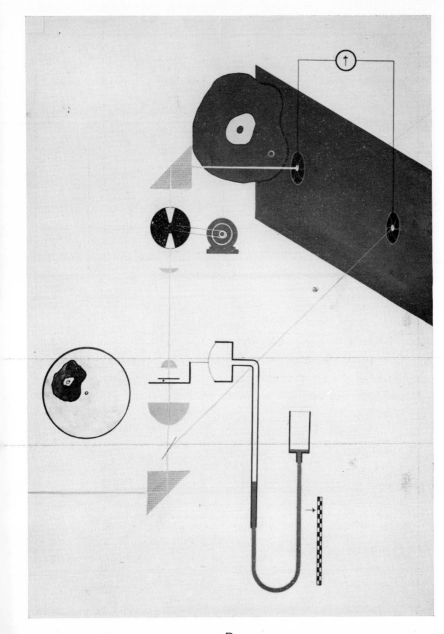

B

B, "Free space" in preparation projected onto photocell, rotating sector partially closed, electric circuit in balance.

35

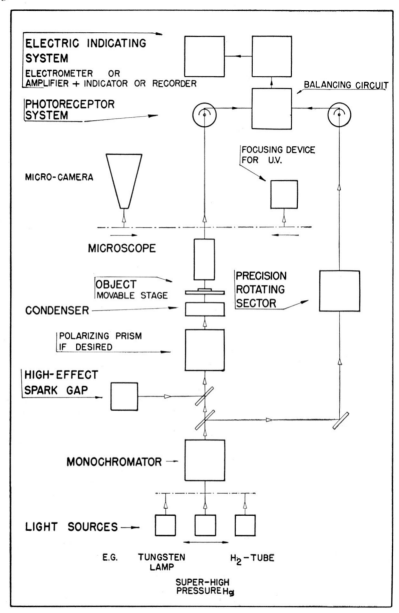

FIGURE 11. Block diagram of arrangement for different wave-length ranges and different degrees of accuracy of instrument in Figure 10.

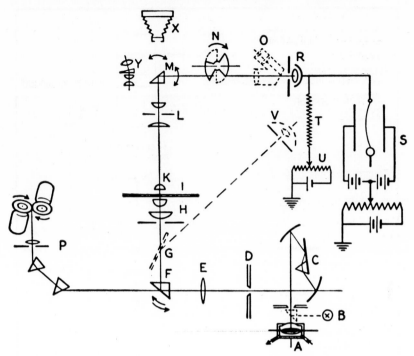

FIGURE 12. Diagram of main instrument used in ultraviolet with high accuracy and high stability, using highly insulated photoelectric cells. A, mercury lamp. B, tungsten band lamp. C, monochromator. D, second monochromator-slit. E, lens. F, movable 90° quartz prism. G, quartz plate (used with photocell V to compensate for changes in the lamp). H, condenser. I, object. K, objective. L, ocular with adjustable diaphragm. M, accurately movable prism of fused quartz. N, rotating sector. O, telescope for centering. P, Köhler's rotating spark gap arrangement. R, photocell. S, electrometer. T, leakage resistance. U, four-step potentiometer. X, camera. Y, Köhler focuser, for the ultraviolet, interchangeable with prism M.

materials. In order to keep the energy falling on the object as low as possible, and also to keep the measuring area as small as possible, the photocell system must be as sensitive as possible. The highly insulated photocells have very high stability and fairly good sensitivity in the ultraviolet region in question. The photoelectric currents put out by them are balanced with an electrometer sufficiently

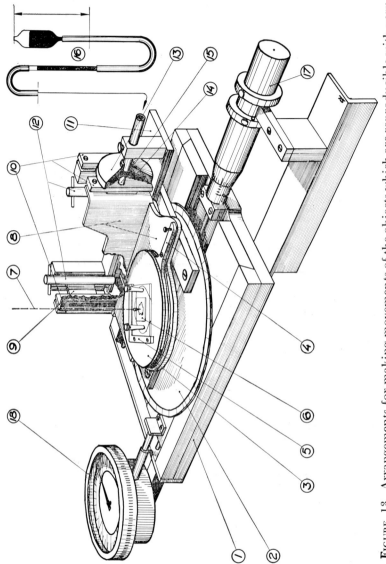

F<small>IGURE</small> 13. Arrangements for making movements of the objects which are reproducible with very high accuracy. (See opposite page for explanation.)

sensitive. The combination of specially manufactured highly insulated quartz cells and Lutz–Edelman string electrometers is extremely convenient in routine work, as it is ready for immediate use at all times. The system can furthermore very easily be shielded from external influences, such as temperature variations and electric or magnetic disturbing fields. This latter is a great advantage when using high-energy light sources fed with high-tension currents, especially through condenser discharges. In the visible regions when stable sources of light are available, vacuum-enclosed amplifying circuits with electrometer tubes in the first step have been used to some advantage. They are not so convenient for routine work as good electrometers, mainly because of the time lost when they are "warming up" and the difficulty in getting perfect shielding when high-energy sparks are used in the neighborhood. They are, however, considerably cheaper. Photomultiplier tubes have much lower insulation resistance than the specially built one-stage photocells. The very high photoelectric yield in some of these tubes to some extent compensates for the lack of insulation, and individually

---

1. Mechanical stage (lateral movement).
2. Mechanical stage (measurable rotary movement).
3. Mechanical stage (rotary movement for adjustment of object clamping device).
4. Fixed support for 3.
5. Slide holder.
6. Slide with object.
7. Optical axis of microscope.
8. Carriage, suspended from quartz plates 9, which supports stage 3 independently of other structures.
9. Quartz plates connecting carriage 8 with supports. The plates support the carriage and serve as springs for its movement.
10. Supports for quartz plates: one pair fixed to base plate 11, the other "floating" and connected to carriage 8.
11. Base plate fixed to rotary stage 2 by two bars and two movable parts of mechanical stage 1 by screw 12.
12. Screw allowing for movement of base plate 11 in relation to stage 2.
13. Membrane house connecting manometric system 16 to steel membrane 14.
14. Steel membrane which transmits manometric pressure changes to steel knob 15, thus moving carriage 8 in relation to base plate 11.
15. Steel knob fixed to carriage 8 and in contact with membrane 14.
16. Manometer arrangement.
17. Fine adjustment for movement of the entire apparatus.
18. Gauge measuring lateral movement in microns.

selected tubes cooled with dry ice approach the arrangement described above in sensitivity, although not in stability. In the ultraviolet, a distinct disadvantage is the great difficulty of making a well-balanced circuit with automatic correction for great and sudden changes in the source of light, for example the spark gap. For the measurement of comparatively large areas, when the light flow is comparatively large and when accuracy need not be high, the photomultiplier tubes may render good service.

The danger of overexposing the preparations during measurement should be emphasized as a factor which largely influences the technical arrangements. With the instrument described, the exposure can be held at a minimum by the following arrangements: Focusing can be made on a part of the preparation other than the point to be measured. The preparation for measurement, such as balancing the circuits, etc., can be done without irradiation of the point to be measured. Because of the irradiation factor, most registering procedures for relations between wave length and extinctions or for integrating measurements are not favorable below 3000 Å. The least damaging procedure for integrating measurement in this wave-length range is thus densitometric evaluation of photographic plates taken with minimal exposures at critical wave lengths. If a photoelectric measurement is taken at individual points in the preparation and combined with the photogrammetric data, the combination can be made to give results of considerably higher accuracy than the photographic procedures alone.

4. SOME COMPLEMENTARY PROCEDURES

In the measurement of absorption, the most important characteristics of the object besides its absorption are its dimensions, its homogeneity, and its refractive properties. *The influence of inhomogeneities* in the preparation is largely eliminated by the reduction of the measured surface to the neighborhood of the theoretical limit—the smallest structure which the microscope can resolve.

The dimensions.—In a plane perpendicular to the axis of the measuring ray the dimensions are easily determined by usual micro-

scope methods. For the measurement of the thickness of an object
the following procedures have been shown most useful: For preparations passing through paraffin, weighing of the sections before
deparaffination; otherwise, measurement of the distance between
coverslip and slide with reflection procedures (*see* Figure 14 and
1947, 1) or, in thin preparations, with the well-known interfero-
metric procedures. This distance is in most cases considerably larger
than the average thickness of the preparation. In order to measure
the actual thickness of the preparation itself, an instrument has been
constructed which is described in Figure 15. The optical pathway
in different parts of the preparation can also be measured with a low
degree of accuracy by the procedure described in Figure 14. It will
probably be possible to make such measurements with higher accuracy and greater convenience with the aid of phase-contrast optics
when we have an arrangement in which the effective thickness of the
phase plate can be regulated continuously.

Refractive index.—The most favorable materials with regard to
light refractions are some living objects (cf. page 57) and preparations made by smearing in fluids containing up to 50 per cent acetic
acid (1936, 1). The refractive index differences in different parts of
such specimens rarely exceed a few hundredths of a unit.

For any large-scale work and work where precise localization is
desirable, however, it is necessary to use fixed, imbedded, and sec-
tioned material. The ideal imbedding medium for this purpose
would have the same refractive index as the protein particles in a
fixed preparation and at the same time be free from absorption,
especially below 3000 Å. Such a medium, however, is not available.
It is thus necessary to try to develop procedures whereby measurements can be made in such material under conditions that are not
ideal. For this, our first task is to analyze the case theoretically.

5. METHODS FOR THE PREPARATION OF THE OBJECT AND THEIR THEORETICAL BACKGROUND (1936, 1; 1940, 1)

For a theoretical treatment of the consequences of these conditions, a fixed biological specimen, transferred to a nonabsorbing

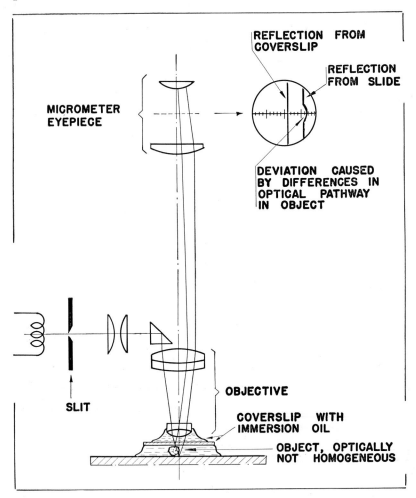

FIGURE 14. Arrangement for measuring the distance between slide and coverslip and also larger refractive index differences in the objects.

(Best results attained with a specially built glycerine immersion system of aperture about 1.0. The optical parts of a recently available commercial instrument for measurement of the smoothness of metal surfaces, the "Raulimeter" from Busch, can be used after minor alterations.)

imbedding fluid, might again be thought of as a system of small spheres suspended in a medium with a different refractive index. The particle size is assumed to be of the order of magnitude of the wave length of light. If we examine an individual particle we find

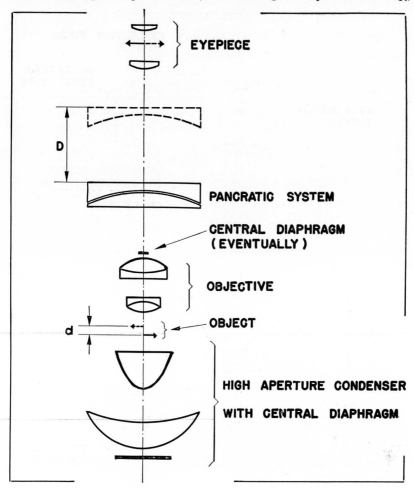

EYEPIECE

D

PANCRATIC SYSTEM

CENTRAL DIAPHRAGM
(EVENTUALLY)

OBJECTIVE

OBJECT

d

HIGH APERTURE CONDENSER

WITH CENTRAL DIAPHRAGM

FIGURE 15. Arrangement for measurement of the distance between two structures in a microscopic preparation in the direction of the microscope axis by subsequent focusing. The focus depth of the microscope is kept very low by a high-power objective and central diaphragms in that and in the condenser (in some materials phase-contrast sets can be used to advantage). The focusing is changed by moving the negative lens, belonging to the pancratic system, and the distance D is a function of the distance between the two planes in the object, subsequently focused. Accuracy to $\frac{1}{5}\mu$. Microscope stand must be very heavy.

that it disperses light according to the curves in Figure 8. These dispersion curves have different shapes in different wave lengths, such that there is more dispersion at shorter wave lengths. That is, under otherwise identical conditions, the side scattering is more pronounced the shorter the wave length (cf. Figure 9A). If the absorption is measured with an instrument which collects only the light within a small space angle, the loss of light, conditioned by the light scattering, will increase with decreasing wave length. As has been shown earlier, the course of the energy-distribution curve around a particle is determined by the size of the particle, the wave length of the light, and the complex refractive index of the particle with respect to its surroundings. The absorption of a suspension of a large number of similar particles, measured with an instrument with *small* aperture, can be calculated and is shown in Figure 9. These graphs show absorption spectra of suspensions of particles of nonabsorbing material. It is evident not only that this absorption generally tends to increase toward shorter wave lengths but also that selective absorption phenomena might occur. This analysis, if applied to protein structures in a histological specimen, will show that, even in the absence of any true absorption, pseudo-selective absorption might be observed, conditioned only by light refraction or scattering. In principle, the phenomenon is similar within the whole range of dimensions from particles smaller than the light wave lengths up to the large particles in the range of geometrical optics. The exact distribution curve for the type case can be taken directly out of the tables in the paper cited above (1932, 2; 1933, 1). The Rayleigh scattering (a loss of light inversely proportional to the fourth power of the wave length) appears as the simplest special case for particles which are infinitely small, compared with the wave length of the light. The other extreme is represented by the loss of light due to refraction in a particle infinitely large as compared with the wave length. Thus loss increases very slowly with decreasing wave length within a limited spectral range, practically proportional to the increase in refractive index (cf. curve 3, Figure 74A).

In the actual measuring of a microscopic specimen, apparent absorptions, such as those in Figure 9, will appear if all the light deflected by the specimen does not enter the aperture of the measuring instrument. If the instrument, however, is arranged so that all light leaving the particle is collected, then that "pseudo-absorption" effect will disappear. It is obviously not possible to obtain such an ideal lens in practical microspectrophotometric work, but by the use of measuring systems with high aperture that source of error can be diminished. This is a further reason for the use of high-aperture lenses in microspectrophotometric work.

The theory indicates two ways for the elimination of these sources of error. As shown in Figure 8, the energy distribution around the light-scattering particle can be presented as a solid body. For an infinitely small particle this body is symmetrical, with regard to a plane through the particle perpendicular to the central ray of light. If the particle diameter increases, the body is deformed by being elongated in the direction of the central ray.

If the refractive index between the sphere and the suspension medium is diminished, a further deformation in the same direction occurs. This means that for a certain aperture of the receiving system a larger percentage of the deflected light enters the lens, the lower the refractive index difference. Thus, the closer we can make the n of the medium to that of our object, the smaller will be the error in our absorption measurement due to refraction and scattering. The energy distribution curves given in Figure 8 are calculated for different particle diameters and for the index 1.18 (with the exception of the lowest one which is calculated for index 1.33). From the figure it is clear that at these very high refractive indices, in order to collect 95 per cent of the light which is scattered *behind* the particle (on the right side of the particle in the figure), it would be necessary to use an aperture close to 2x90 degrees.

In practical work on cell material, the imbedding medium preferable to all others is double distilled glycerine. Experience shows that the extreme refractive index ratios in ultraviolet in specimens prepared in this medium often reach 1.10, but that in most cases they can be kept below this number by the use of the technique described below for the elimination of back-scattering. In most fixed preparations, such as formalin-treated ones, the index ratio in glycerine is still higher. This makes the index ratio 1.10 a practical limit for which one has to be prepared. Any cell material must be prepared and the instrument must be built so as to give absorption data which can be analyzed even at that index ratio. Figure 16 (1936, 1) presents the flow of light energy in a particle as a function of the angle of deflection from the direction of the incident light

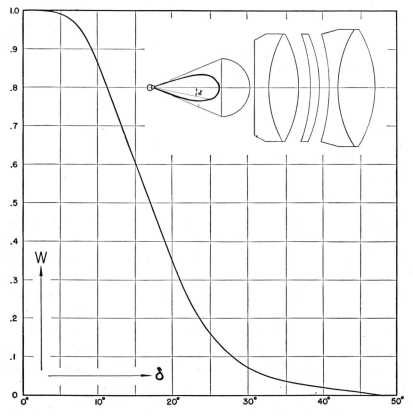

FIGURE 16. Light dispersion behind object in relation to aperture of lens. Inserted: Diagram of object and lens. Curve: Energy distribution in different azimuths around object. The surface under the curve gives the total energy falling within a cone with the top angle 2δ.

(cf. inserted small diagram above). Thus the area under the curve between two δ-values is the total flow of light energy within that space angle. The index ratio is 1.10. The figure shows that if the lens catches at least 95 per cent of the light, its opening must be 2x30 degrees. Thus, this is the absolute minimum in aperture for microspectrographic work, aiming at curve analysis (e.g., determination of proteins in the presence of nucleotides).

In the case treated it was assumed that the incident light was parallel. In the practical work an extremely narrow condenser diaphragm would give disturbing diffraction phenomena in the immediate neighborhood of phase borderlines and would also have certain other disadvantages. In order not to complicate the evaluation of the absorption data all the rays should pass the object as closely perpendicular to its plane as conveniently possible. The maximum angle permissible is a matter of choice, depending on the object and the light intensity available. As the upper limit in the routine work, 10 degrees has been chosen. At this condenser aperture the way the obliquest ray has to pass through the object is 2 per cent longer than that of the central ray and the over-all error introduced in the measurement of extinction as compared with parallel light will be negligible.

The angular aperture of the condenser system has to be added to that of the objective in the calculation above. Thus the minimum angular opening of the lens must be 2x40 degrees, corresponding to a numerical aperture of 0.85. This value of the numerical aperture is an absolute minimum value for microspectrographic work, aiming at curve analysis. Since the errors increase very rapidly with sinking aperture (*see* Figure 16, steep part of curve), it can hardly be stressed enough that *with the fixing agents and imbedding media at present available an absorption curve measured with systems having aperture lower than 0.85 is of very limited value.*

Figure 8 demonstrates that a considerable part of the light deflected from small particles goes backwards as well. This part cannot be collected by usual lens optics and would offer great difficulties even for reflection optics. The percentage of back-scattered light is smallest for the large particles, but is quite considerable for the small particles. At the index ratio of 1.56 : 1.33 (glass : water) the intensity ratio between light scattered in the direction of the central beam and that scattered in the opposite direction is about 64:1 for the case of infinitely large particles. For the particle diameter 0.2μ, however, the ratio is 10:1 and for a diameter of 0.1μ, the ratio is 2:1.

A closer analysis of the conditions for light reflection shows a way to eliminate even this source of error. If we at first look at the particle to which geometrical optics can be applied, then the back-scattered light arises by reflections at the surface of the particle. Now, reflection occurs only at boundaries characterized by a sudden jump in refractive index—a jump which has to occur within a distance that is small compared with the wave length of the light. If we could change all such sharp boundaries into continuous changes of refractive index from the value in the one phase to that in the other, then the primary condition for the appearance of the reflection phenomenon would be eliminated. For smaller particles, the light deflection of which can only be calculated with due regard to the light scattering (that is, according to the complete theory of Mie), a discussion can be carried through which in principle is the same and leads to similar results.

This means that, if the jump in refractive index between a protein particle in the fixed preparation and the imbedding medium could be exchanged for a continuous transition from one refractive index to the other, it would be possible to eliminate largely the back-scattering. After considerable work with different media a simple satisfactory procedure has been developed for this purpose (1940, 1). The tissues or the cells to be investigated are frozen-dried and imbedded, preferably in paraffin. After deparaffination, the sections are transferred into pure double distilled glycerine and are measured in this medium. In order to alter the internal cell structure as little as possible, the freezing-drying procedure should be arranged, for instance, according to Altmann and Gersh with freezing in isopentane at the temperature of liquid air and subsequent drying in vacuum at –40 degrees over phosphorus pentoxide. The transfer to glycerine can be made in different ways. In the glycerine the cell proteins which are not coagulated by the preceding treatment slowly begin to swell. In *water-free* glycerine this swelling occurs so slowly that in most tissues a transport of material can be observed in the microscope only after the lapse of many hours. In the first few minutes, however, the sharp index jump between protein particles and imbedding medium is changed into a continuous transition and the back-scattering is diminished to a very large extent. The effect of these procedures is exemplified in Figure 17, A, B, and C. In these figures all extinctions are plotted logarithmically so as to demonstrate the *shapes* of the curves with the influence of the concentration eliminated. In all cases absolute values of abscissae are arbitrarily chosen. In B and C, the upper curves show the absorption of mixtures of serum globulin and diiodotyrosine (B) and of mixtures of serum globulin and ribodesose polynucleotide (C), measured in a usual spectrograph. The lower curves are taken in the microspectrograph of histological section of the same mixtures, but frozen-dried and imbedded in paraffin. The course of the curves agrees very well and shows that with the procedure described above the influence of light scattering and refraction can be largely eliminated. That the main factor, thereby, is the swelling and disappearance of the interphasial boundaries and not the mere freezing-drying procedure is demonstrated by the curves in A. A (curve I) gives the absorption of the optically very homogeneous thyroid colloid, measured in glycerine on a section by the procedure mentioned above. A (curve II) is the absorption spectrum found in the same way on another section of the same block, but immersed in paraffin oil. In spite of the higher refractive index of the latter medium a very pronounced light-scattering effect appears, resulting in a change in the course of the absorption curve measured and rapidly increasing with falling wave length.

In view of the decisive importance of the objective receiving practically all the light from the object, a special device is recommended for the measurement of the light distribution around the object. The object to be measured (*see* Figure 18) is put on the stage

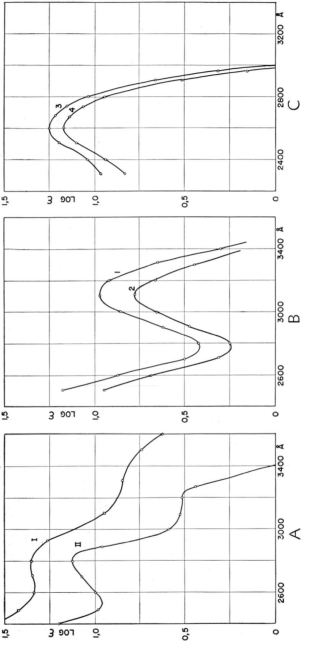

FIGURE 17. A (curve I): Thyroid colloid, measured according to procedure described in the text. A (curve II): Same object, measured after immersion in paraffin oil. Great loss of light, causing false absorption effects, rapidly increasing with falling wave lengths. B (curve 1): Mixture of thyroglobulin and diiodotyrosine, measured in usual macrospectrograph. B (curve 2): Same solution, frozen-dried and treated according to procedure described in text. C, Mixture of serum globulin and nucleic acid, otherwise the same as B. Absorption curves logarithmically plotted in order to facilitate comparison of shape. Ordinate arbitrarily chosen.

In the technical work it is necessary for the instrument used to conform to certain requirements, the most important of which are:

(1) The accuracy of measurement must be high.

(2) Measurement must be possible in a large number of wave lengths, preferably in a continuous spectrum, including a range where the object has no true absorption. For work on proteins a continuous spectrum must be available between 2600 Å. and 3100 Å.

(3) The optical system itself must fulfill several conditions. The most important are that the aperture must exceed a certain value and that the optics should fulfill Abbe's sine condition.

(4) The optical conditions in the object must be controlled and known. It is very desirable to know the light-scattering curve of the object in the area to be measured. If the optical constants are not known, the experiments should be planned with due regard to the errors which might result. Any measurements with arrangements which do not fulfill these conditions introduce different sources of error which cannot be fully eliminated.

Comments on these different points:

Ad (1) and (2).—The goal of each measurement is the analysis of the curves. At first the absorption curve is broken up into its individual absorbing components and the curve given by the light scattering in the preparation. This is done by simple proportions, using absorption data in a number of wave lengths determined by the number of components in the curve. In the wave-length range below 3000 Å. the selective absorptions have as a rule a steep slope and in different wave lengths the absorptions of certain substances largely dominate over those of other materials. It is thus necessary to make the measurement of transmission with high accuracy. (Example: Assume that the mixture of nucleotides and a protein with 5% tyrosine and 1% tryptophane is to be determined in the wave lengths most advantageous for ratio determination, 2600 Å. and 2800 Å. and in a preparation with 1.5% nucleotides. If the absorption at 2600 Å. is 83% [transmission 17%], an error of 1% would give 84% absorption [transmission 16%], and the calculated value of the nucleotide concentration would be 20% too high).

For the same reason it is always necessary to be able to use not only the most advantageous wave lengths for the individual case, but also to have at one's disposal enough wave lengths to get safe determinations.

Ad (3).—The optical system must fulfill a series of conditions, the most important of which are that Abbe's sine condition is fulfilled and that the aperture of the measuring system is high. The main reasons for the latter conditions are: (a) The definition of the image must be perfect, and the resolving power of the lens must be such that the structure to be measured is clearly defined. (b) All the light leaving the structure to be measured must participate in forming the image, otherwise the intensity distribution in the image will not correspond to that in the object. (c) All the light leaving the part of the object around the measured structure should participate in the formation of the image. Otherwise a false absorption will appear, which at low apertures can even have the appearance of selective absorption.

Ad (4).—The optical conditions in the object must be well controlled and known in order to insure that there will be no loss of light by scattering, etc., which cannot be accounted for and corrected. Preferably the light scattering in various directions of space from the area around the point to be measured should be estimated. (A special instrument for that purpose is shown in Figure 18).

For practical work, conditions (3) and (4) mean that if we have an especially suitable material, fixed as described above and treated according to the freezing-drying procedure already explained, measurement of the content of nucleotides and selectively absorbing amino acids can only be done with lenses having a *numerical aperture of at least 0.85*. Measurements on other materials, for instance formalin-fixed material in glycerine, with that minimum aperture can give only a crude picture of the distribution of the most heavily absorbing substances, if no corrections are made for the loss of light. They can, however, be of considerable value for comparative studies in the same or in similar preparations.

Corrections for losses of light due to insufficient aperture are difficult and should be avoided as far as possible by the use of large apertures and proper treatment of the object. The simplest way to estimate the loss is to carry the measurement through a spectral region where the object exerts no specific absorption and then to extrapolate that nonspecific absorption over the region of a true absorption. A more promising method is to determine the distribution of scattered light around the object by an instrument like the one in Figure 18 and then, using the data cited above, to make the proper corrections.

For discussion of the validity of Beer's law, the influence of anomalous dispersion, etc., the reader is referred to the original papers. It should be pointed out that it is rarely possible to get reliable data on the validity of Beer's law for a given substance at very high concentrations and in fixed specimens (for nucleotides and proteins *see* original papers). Another factor of still higher practical importance is the shrinking of the object by the fixing agent. Volume shrinkages of one-third are not uncommon, for which the reader is referred to the current histological literature on the subject.

In spite of these difficulties it is, however, very often possible to attack a given biological problem, even when the optical data are incomplete, by arranging the experiment so that two identically treated specimens, or still better two places in the same specimen, have to be compared. Another way, which is as a rule the most convenient one, is to arrange the experiment so that the magnitude of the effect to be measured (e.g., difference in concentration of one absorbing compound) is of a much greater magnitude than any errors arising from the factors discussed. As an example of the former method the comparisons of gland cells in different stages of activity can be used, and for the latter method an example is a study of nucleotides in epithelial tumors mentioned below (Chapter VI; 1942, 2). In the latter case, the only material available, giving the wide scope necessary for the plan of study, was the routinely formalin-fixed specimens collected at pathological institutes. The differences in nucleotide concentrations in the cells in different stages of growth (*see* Figures 73 and 74) were so enormous that they could be ascertained in spite of the unsuitable fixation technique.

7. TREATMENT OF THE OBJECTS IN THE INVESTIGATIONS

For the data to be given in later chapters, the arrangement described above for absorption measurements has been used. It fulfills conditions (1) and (2) in paragraph 6. As to condition (3), apertures of 0.85 have been used in most cases, and for the smallest structures 1.25. In order to fulfill condition (4) and also to be able to transfer the data to the living object whenever feasible, the work has been arranged as follows:

(1) The living cell is studied in the ultraviolet microscope and when desirable photographed on standardized plates in a chosen number of wave lengths in order to serve for integrating measurements or as comparisons with observations according to (3) and (4) below.

(2) Comparisons are made of the photographed cells in a living material with those in frozen and dried preparations.

(3) Measurements are made on frozen-dried preparations.

(4) Observations and measurements of the same preparation are made, comparing the results of different types of extraction, where possible on materials with different types of fixation. This procedure is an attempt to eliminate the influence of absorbing substances other than those to be studied. If we wish to study nucleic acid and protein we will thus have to extract mononucleotides, oligonucleotides and sterols.

A number of complementary procedures, smaller and more technical, have to be used for the work in the ultraviolet (cf. Chapter II, paragraph 4 and Chapter III). Microdissection is a most advantageous way of preparing small parts of cells for optical cytochemical work. Ultracentrifugation, eventually followed by microdissection, is another useful method.

It should be pointed out that these absorption procedures can be used for the study of a variety of different substances. Here I will refer only to the work on nucleotides and proteins. I should, how-

ver, at this point like to refer to the work done on the localization
f thyroxine and tyrosine derivatives by Gersh and Caspersson,
1940, 5), ATP by Thorell and Caspersson (1941, 6), and lignin by
ange (1944, 7; 1945, 7). Several other substances have also been
udied. The procedure has also been used for other purposes, for
istance the determination of the orientation of light-absorbing
symmetric molecules in biological material (*see* Figure 19 and
940, 3, 4; 1944, 7; 1945, 7).

Within the visible region a number of questions arise. Absorp-
ions are, as a rule, very low at the thickness of single cells. A special
rrangement for precise measurement of very small absorptions
as been used in preliminary experiments for measuring the dis-
ribution of respiratory enzymes, for instance cytochrome, with
he instrument in Figure 30 (1940, 1). Still more, this region has
een used for the measurement of the uptake of different stains by
ell structures, either directly in the cell or after their release by
uitable solvents from the cell structures.

The living cell is, as a rule, an unsuitable object for microspectro-
hotometric studies. The reasons are (a) it is very motile, (b) great
ructural changes occur during irradiation, and (c) for most prob-
ems, suitably extracted objects give the cleanest data. The changes
uring irradiation are of another kind than in the fixed specimen.
n the living nucleus, refractive index differences up to several hun-
redths of a unit occur, but because of continuous changes in the
idex from place to place (cf. the discussion above in paragraph 5),
hey are not very clear to the eye in the ordinary microscope. After
hort irradiation with ultraviolet light partial coagulation phe-
omena appear, resulting in contraction of certain parts, mainly
hose carrying nucleic acid. From that two effects follow: (1) Inter-
hase boundaries appear, resulting in light scattering and refrac-
ion and a general *not selective* increase in absorption, most pro-
ounced in the shorter wave lengths and overlaying the "true"
bsorption. This effect is sometimes very great and has even been
alsely interpreted as an appearance of new absorbing compounds at
he death of the cell. A measurement of the absorption spectrum of
he nucleus reveals immediately that the increase in absorption is a

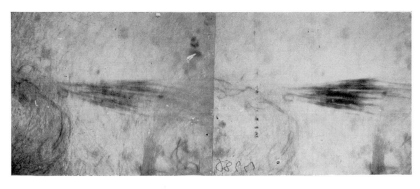

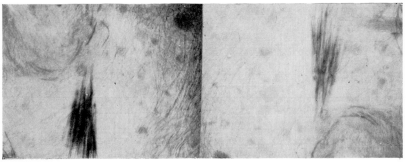

A

Figure 19. A, Bundle of sperm heads from Chorthippus, photographed in polarized light at 2570 Å. with the polarization plane respectively parallel (upper right) and perpendicular (lower left) to the sperm axis (cf. 1940, 4).

pure optical illusion. (2) During the contraction of the chromatin granules, for example, their absorption increases because the light ray passes through more substance in the same granule after the shrinkage than before. Assume a sphere 5μ in diameter and with an absorption of the central ray of 50 per cent of the light. If that granule contracts to the diameter 3μ, the concentration of absorbing substances increases $(5:3)^3 = 4.6$ times. The distance traversed by the central ray of light has diminished only to 3 from $5\mu = 1.7$ times. The resulting light absorption will then be 80 per cent instead of 50 per cent. *Contractions of this order of magnitude are common and most impressive to the eye (see* Figure 20). *The two effects men-*

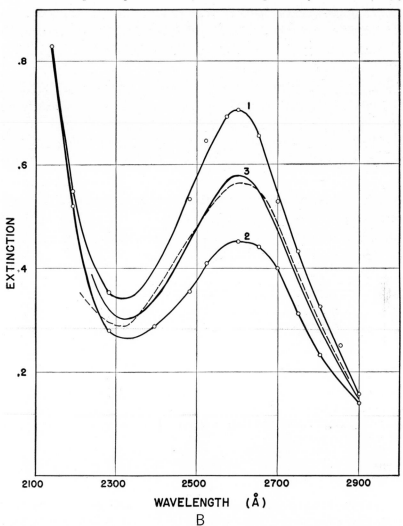

B (curves 1 and 2): Absorption spectra of film of oriented ribodesose nucleotide microspectrophotometrically measured with polarized ultraviolet light (equipment in Figure 11). In curve 1 the polarization plane is parallel to and in curve 2 perpendicular to the long axis of the molecules. Curve 3 gives the average of 1 and 2 and the dotted curve is the absorption of the same film measured with unpolarized light.

*tioned underline, furthermore, the necessity for quantitative work
with light absorptions and cell dimensions before any chemical interpretations are put on absorption changes.*

8. ARRANGEMENT OF ILLUSTRATIONS

In the following presentation ultraviolet photographs mainly are
chosen for demonstration. *The reader is referred to the original
papers for the corresponding quantitative absorption data.* When
not designated otherwise, the photographs were taken at 2570 Å.
with a lens aperture of 0.85 and focal length 2.5 mm. The condenser
opening is 0.4. Magnification originally was 1000 times. Throughout, the ultraviolet microscope developed by A. Köhler has been
used. The optics developed by him and von Rohr have also been
used in the microspectrograph.

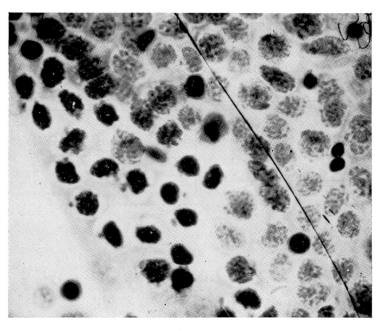

FIGURE 20. Photograph at 2570 Å. of groups of identical cells (spermatocytes in a smear preparation of surviving testis from Myrmus). The
darker cells on the left side of the dark line have been killed by previous
irradiation of that field and show a conspicuous increase in absorption,
solely caused by the optical factor mentioned in Chapter II, paragraph 7.

CHAPTER III

Microspectrography of nucleotides and proteins (1936, 1; 1940, 3)

1. DETERMINATION OF NUCLEOTIDES, TYROSINE, TRYPTO-PHANE AND THE SUM OF ACYCLIC AMINO ACIDS

THERE ARE two groups of cell substances that are more easily studied by microspectrographic procedures than any others. These are the proteins, especially those containing cyclic amino acids, and the polynucleotides (1934, 1; 1935, 1). The specific absorption of these substances is of such an order of magnitude that in layers no thicker than those we generally use in histological preparations, and in the concentrations in which they occur in the cells, the resulting total absorptions are easy to determine in the part of the ultraviolet spectrum between 2400 Å. and 3000 Å. Moreover, experience has shown that in this region the absorption of almost all other constituents of the cell is so low that it can often be disregarded in the analysis of the absorption curves. I will, however, emphasize that it is always necessary to have complete absorption spectra from material treated in different ways (cf. Chapter II, paragraph 7). All the data I present here are founded on such complete studies, using both absorption microspectrophotometry and complementary procedures.

Figure 21A (curve II) shows the absorption spectrum in long-wave ultraviolet of human serum globulin, chosen as a type for the animal proteins. The band at 2800 Å. is determined by the presence

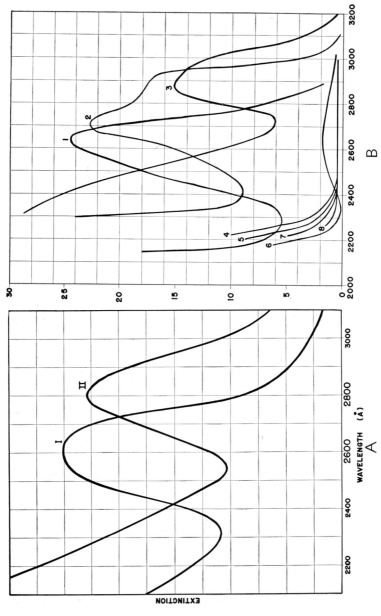

FIGURE 21. A, Curve I shows absorption spectra of polynucleotides. Curve II shows serum globulin. B, Absorption spectra of (1) adenine, (2) tryptophane, (3) tyrosine, (4) histidine, (5) arginine, (6) phenylalanine, (7) leucylglycin, (8) proline. (Adenine ⅓%, the others 1%, 1 cm. thickness of layer.)

in the protein molecule of certain cyclic amino acids, primarily tyrosine, tryptophane and phenylalanine.

The absorption of the compound protein is the sum of the absorption of its component amino acids, Figure 22A (for references and details *see* 1940, 3; 1947, 1). Small differences in the position of the absorption maximum are found under certain conditions. Such

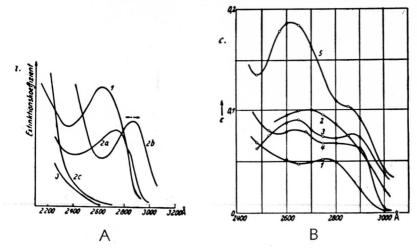

A   B

FIGURE 22. A, The quantitatively most important absorbing constituents of the tissue ultraviolet absorption: (1) nucleic acids, (2a) tryptophane, (2b) tyrosine (the position of the maximum being influenced by the mode of linkage and the *p*H), (2c) other amino acids, (3) light scattering and refraction. B, Some examples of absorption spectra of different types: (1) interband space from salivary gland chromosome, pure protein band; (2) ergastoplasm from a pancreatic cell, nucleotide band plus protein band of the type given by coagulable tissue proteins; (3 and 4) nucleoli from various tissues, low nucleic-acid band plus high band given by proteins rich in hexone bases; (5) chromocenter from salivary gland nucleus, high nucleic-acid band of proteins rich in hexone bases (1942, 2).

a phenomenon has been used as an indication of the presence of high amounts of diamino acids.

Of the two important groups of *polynucleotides,* ribodesose and ribose nucleic acids, the former was shown in 1934 to be held back by ultrafilters with a pore size permitting serum proteins to pass rapidly, indicating that it exists as very large particles in solution (1934, 3). Starting from that observation, studies of the double refraction of flow made with Signer's method showed a very high molecular weight and very long chain molecules (1938, 1). X-ray diffraction studies by Astbury and Bell (*Nature* 141:122, 1938) gave further details and showed the molecule to consist of mononucleotide chains, arranged with a linear spacing that is in close agreement with the spacing found in extended polypeptide chains. There are indications that linear high-molecular complexes are also formed by the ribose acids, but they are not very stable and probably have relatively small molecules (cf. 1940, 4; 1941, 1).

The nucleic acids have a very high absorption in ultraviolet at 2600 Å. conditioned by the conjugated double bonds in the pyrimidine part of the molecule (Figure 21A, curve I).

Practically the same absorption is given by various mononucleotides and polynucleotides. The position of the polynucleotide absorption band is remarkably stable, and it shifts very little, for instance with the pH (1936, 1). On the other hand the influence of external factors on the absorption of mononucleotides is considerable.

The absorption of the nucleotides is so high that the 2600 Å. band entirely dominates the protein band in a solution with comparable concentrations of both substances (Figure 23A). If the absorption is calculated for solutions of nucleic acids and proteins in 5μ layers (a thickness often used in histological specimens), one gets the curves in Figure 23B (1936, 1). It should be noted that even very high protein concentration in this thickness of layers cannot give absorptions at 2600 Å. comparable with the absorption of a 5 per cent solution of nucleic acids. It is thus to be expected that even in an ultraviolet photograph at 2600 Å. the nucleic-acid-rich structures will be much more prominent than the surrounding protein masses.

Figure 24 shows a photograph taken at 2600 Å. of a living pollen mother cell from Tradescantia. The upper curve gives the absorption of a point in such a chromosome, and the lower curve gives the absorption curve of a small arbitrarily chosen area in the cytoplasm. The former shows a clear absorption band at the nucleotide absorption maximum and also a hump at the maximum of the cyclic amino acids. The lower curve shows only a protein absorption.

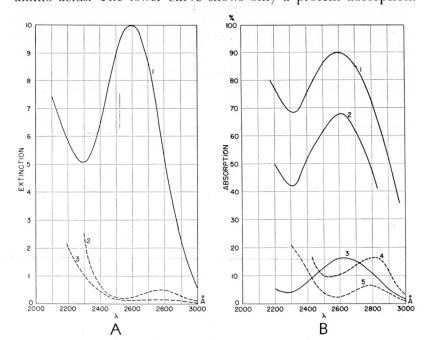

FIGURE 23. Comparison between absorption of nucleic acids and proteins in similar concentrations. A shows (1) thymonucleic acid, 1 cm. and 0,5%o; (2) serum albumin, 0,5%o; (3) protamine sulphate, 5%o. B, Light absorption in per cent of 5μ layers of thymonucleic acid and serum albumin in the concentrations of (1) 10% NA, (2) 5% NA, (3) 1% NA, (4) 10% serum albumin, (5) 25% serum albumin (1936, 1, p. 33).

Figure 25 gives two important examples in which we have nucleic-acid-rich structures, in the nucleus in one case and in the cytoplasm in the other. The first object is a group of cells from a grasshopper testis. The object is photographed at a series of different wave lengths, indicated by the lines in the chart. The corresponding absorption curves are plotted in the diagram. Corresponding photographs from a group of nurse cells from Drosophila are arranged in the lower row.

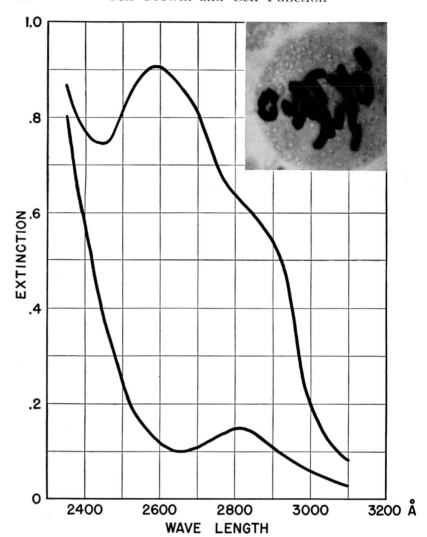

FIGURE 24. Living pollen mother cell from Tradescantia. Upper curve demonstrates general course of the absorption of points in chromosomes (devoid of cytoplasm) and lower curve of points in cytoplasm.

The analysis of the absorption curve is made in principle only, according to the simple rule of three. The *minimum* number of points necessary for the determination of the five components (nucleotides, tyrosine, tryptophane, acyclic amino acids, light scattering) in an ordinary compound absorption curve for a cell is 5. It would be going too far into technical details to present the procedure here; therefore, the reader is referred to the detailed presentation in 1940, 3. One determination cited from that comprehensive paper is given in Figure 26.

2. DETERMINATION OF TOTAL PROTEIN AND NUCLEOTIDE AMOUNTS

The necessity of high accuracy is most evident when one aims at a complete analysis of the curves, as in the presentation above. If it is desirable in a series of preparations to get only relative values on the amounts of nucleic acids and of proteins, or the sum thereof, which comprise practically all the material in the preparations treated as described above, it is sometimes not necessary to go to such extremes in the measurements. Three wave lengths are especially suitable for such determinations, as is evident from Figure 21A, namely 2800 Å., 2600 Å. and 2300 Å. By good luck, three of the brightest lines for the cadmium spark lie close to these points (2750 Å., 2570 Å. and 2310 Å.) and in parts of the early work, for instance that presented in Figure 64 and in the entire tumor work, the very convenient procedure made possible by this fact has been used (for details see 1942, 2, p. 38). If the extinction coefficients per mass unit of the protein and the nucleic acids in two of the wave lengths are respectively $\epsilon_{prot\lambda1}$, $\epsilon_{prot\lambda2}$, $\epsilon_{na\lambda1}$ and $\epsilon_{na\lambda2}$ and the mass per square μ M_{prot} and M_{na}, these amounts are determined by the following equation:

$$E_{measured\lambda1} = M_{na} \cdot \epsilon_{na\lambda1} + M_{prot} \cdot \epsilon_{prot\lambda1} ;$$

$$E_{measured\lambda2} = M_{na} \cdot \epsilon_{na\lambda2} + M_{prot} \cdot \epsilon_{prot\lambda2}.$$

These equations are most easily plotted graphically (see 1942, 2, p. 38), so that after taking measurements in two wave lengths one gets directly the amount of nucleotides and proteins in milligrams per square micron. The most convenient wave lengths are 2570 Å. and 2750 Å., if the absorption spectrum of the protein or its content

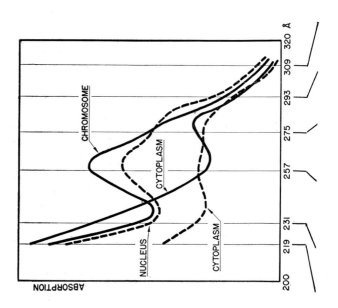

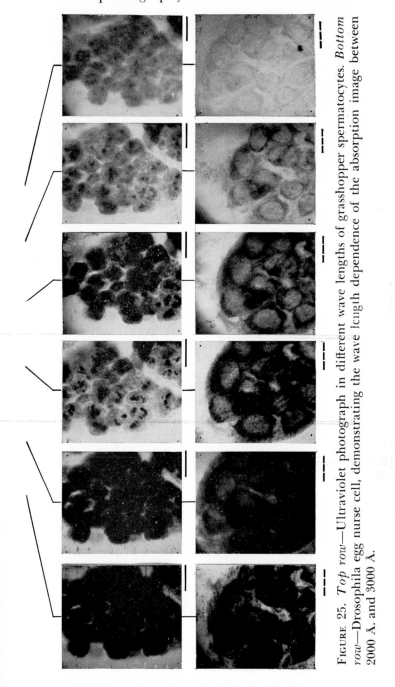

FIGURE 25. *Top row*—Ultraviolet photograph in different wave lengths of grasshopper spermatocytes. *Bottom row*—Drosophila egg nurse cell, demonstrating the wave length dependence of the absorption image between 2000 Å. and 3000 Å.

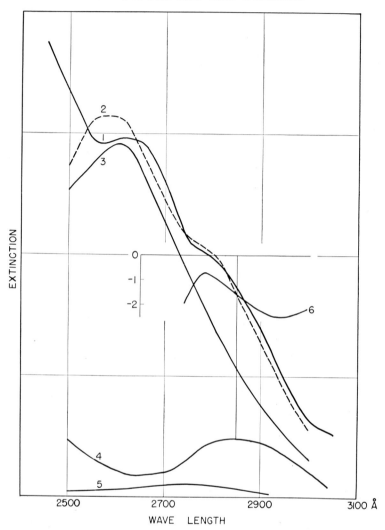

FIGURE 26. Example of analysis of compound curve (1940, 3, p. 583). Heterochromatic part of chromosome in a Drosophila salivary gland. Curve 1, measured absorption; curve 3, nucleic acid component; curve 4, tyrosine component; curve 5, tryptophane component; and curve 2 shows the sum of the components. The small curve 6 is a construction for the localization of the place of the tyrosine band. Results: tyrosine about $0{,}1 \cdot 10^{-10}$ mg., tryptophane $0{,}04 \cdot 10^{-10}$ mg., nucleic acid $0{,}6 \cdot 10^{-10}$ mg. per square micron. Light refraction and diffraction is in this special case negligible as special experiments have shown.

of cyclic amino acids is known. If that is not the case, the pair 2570
Å. and 2310 Å. has to be used since the absorption at these wave
lengths is only to a small extent influenced by selective absorptions of the cyclic amino acids.

The proper procedure in large-scale work is to take complete
absorption spectra of a series of points, thus determining the average protein absorption curve and the average light dispersion, and
then to do the other quantitative work needed in two wave lengths.
Then one gets directly the amount of protein material and of nucleotides in each point investigated. As most such investigations aim
at the determination of the *total sum of material* in one cell or one
cell structure, the most convenient procedure is to work photographically and to determine the absorption in a registering densitometer,
as described above, in a number of tracks across the cell image. With
suitably chosen conditions for the exposure, different for each kind
of plate, one can arrange so that the surface under the curve of the
recording instrument, measured with a planimeter, multiplied with
a constant factor, gives directly the amount of the substances in question along the track of the recording densitometer. In that way, for
instance, the otherwise very laborious determinations (described in
Chapter IV, paragraph 6) of the nucleotide masses in salivary gland
chromosomes were made technically feasible.

3. COMPLEMENTARY PROCEDURES USED

Before entering into the metabolism of the cell, it should be
noted that ultraviolet microspectrophotometry alone is not enough
for studies as extensive as those to be presented. Attention has already been drawn to the combination with extraction procedures.
Many other complementary procedures have been used, for instance the Feulgen microchemical reaction for qualitative determination of the distribution of the ribodesose type of nucleotides
(Figure 27). This method cannot safely be used for quantitative
determinations because of the complexity of the factors determining the kinetics of the reaction (*see* 1932, 1). Digestion procedures
with special enzyme preparations developed by Hammarsten (for

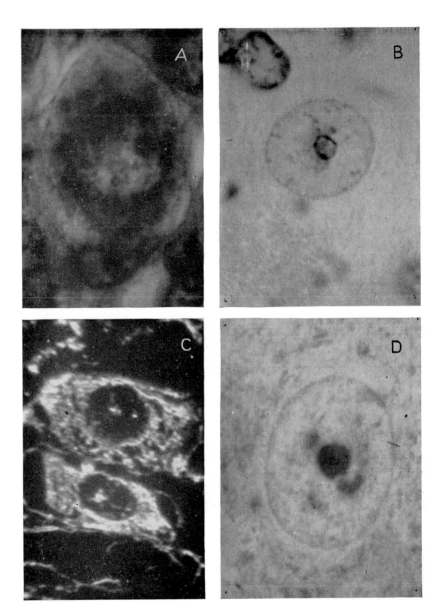

FIGURE 27. Nerve cells: A, ultraviolet photograph. B, Feulgen reaction, showing the localization of the main ribodesose polynucleotides. C, microincineration, indicating general distribution of ashes, of which the main part in this special case consists of phosphates (cf. Engström 1943, 1). D, determination of the distribution of basic amino acids (cf. Hydén, 1943, 5).

details *see* 1935, 1; 1936, 1) enable us to digest away proteins without attacking the ribodesose polynucleotides (Figure 28). Semiquantitative procedures for the localization of diamino acids, using the dyes developed by Greenberg and Smith, have been described

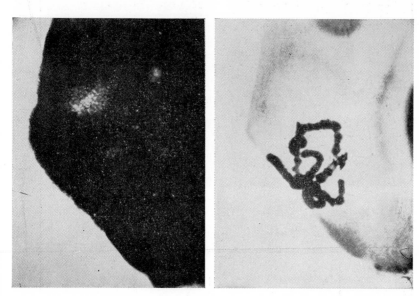

FIGURE 28. Salivary gland cell of Drosophila larva before and after digestion, photographed at 2570 Å. (1936, 1).

by Hydén (1943, 5). Norberg (1942, 4) has developed an ultramicrocolorimetric procedure for determination of phosphates, which enables us to determine various phosphate fractions in small amounts of tissues, in individual cells, or even in some cases in individual chromosomes (Figures 29, 30). Also, simple microincineration can sometimes be of use (1943, 1).

For cytochemical studies of this kind it is most desirable to have a standard system, such as protein nitrogen or weight of specimen, to which to refer the data for comparison. For that reason an X-ray spectrographic procedure has recently been developed by Engström. By aid of this the total mass of a cell structure can be determined in a preparation also suitable for analysis with other optical cytochemical procedures. Furthermore several elements can be

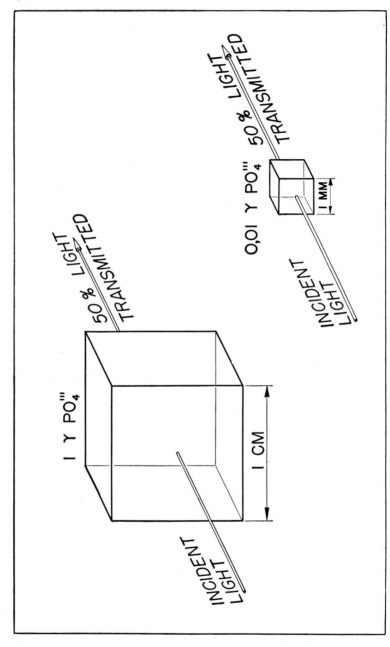

FIGURE 29. The principle of ultramicrocolorimetry. By making the color reaction in very small volumes, a very great increase in sensitivity can be attained.

ARRANGEMENT FOR THE MEASUREMENT OF
VERY SMALL ABSORPTIONS WITH HIGH ACCURACY

HIGH STABILITY VACUUM ENCLOSED AMPLIFIER
FOR CURRENTS DOWN TO 10^{-15} AMPS

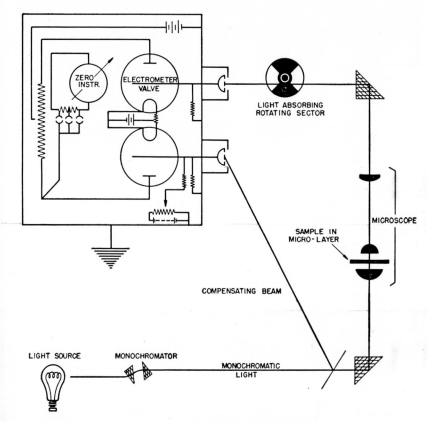

FIGURE 30. Arrangement used by Norberg for ultramicrocolorimetry.

determined under the same conditions (Figure 31). Engström's methods represent an important technical development for the cytochemical approach in general (1946, 3, 4; 1947, 2, 3, 4, 5; 1948, 2).

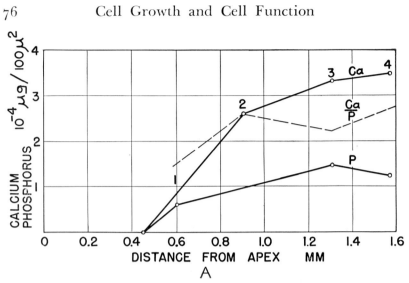

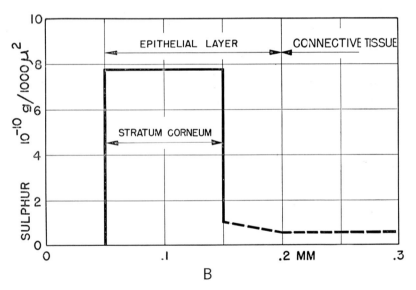

FIGURE 31. A, X-ray microspectrographic determinations according to Engström of Ca and P in dentine cells at different levels in a guinea pig tooth. B, Sulphur distribution in a transverse section of human skin.

In summary, we may say that for the purpose of studying nucleic acid and protein metabolism we can, with ultraviolet microspectrophotometry, determine the amount of polynucleotides and cyclic amino acids with good accuracy, the sum of other amino acids less accurately, and can get an estimate of the amount of diamino acids (for discussions on this point *see* 1947, 1). With supplementary procedures we can distinguish between structures carrying ribose and ribodesose nucleotides and can also get complementary data on the distribution of various fractions of phosphates and amino acids.

With regard to the following presentation it cannot be stressed enough that only the evaluation of absorption spectra, taken with the proper procedures, are of any use in the work on nucleotide and protein distribution in the cell. Single photographs and absorption curves taken in only a few wave lengths are of no or very limited value. All the following data, even those illustrated only with photographs, are founded entirely on absorption measurements. The main fallacy of simple microscopy is the very great differences in protein concentration in different cells and different cell organelles which range from more than 40 per cent, as in some nucleolar substances for example, down to a few per cent, as in the cytoplasm of some gland cells.

CHAPTER IV

Protein metabolism under the mitotic cycle*
(1940, 3; 1941, 2)

THE MOST important periods in the life of a cell can be said to be the stage of cell division and the stage of growth and function. They are also described as the mitotic phase and the interphase (meaning the time between two mitotic periods). During the stage of cell division, the gene material is distributed to daughter nuclei with the aid of a special, complicated mechanism. In connection with this process a reproduction of the genes, that is, an augmentation of the gene protein, occurs. After the end of the mitotic phase the cell has divided into two daughter cells, generally of the same size, and so the mass of the individual cells has been diminished to one-half that of the original cell. During the mitotic phase no increase of cell mass occurs. During the interphase the daughter cells grow and reach, as a rule, the size of the mother cells. There is a real increase of cell mass that includes the protein in the nucleus as well as in the cell body. With regard to protein metabolism, the process of mitosis is dominated by a redistribution of the proteins in the nuclei, including those of the genes themselves. The interphase picture is dominated by the augmentation of the protein masses of the cell body.

Figure 32 shows a typical not-dividing interphase tissue cell, an interphase cell from mammalian liver. Absorption curves are plotted on the side of the photograph in order to indicate their

---

* The author is indebted to Dr. Hans Bauer for many valuable discussions at the time when the views in the two following chapters were developed.

78

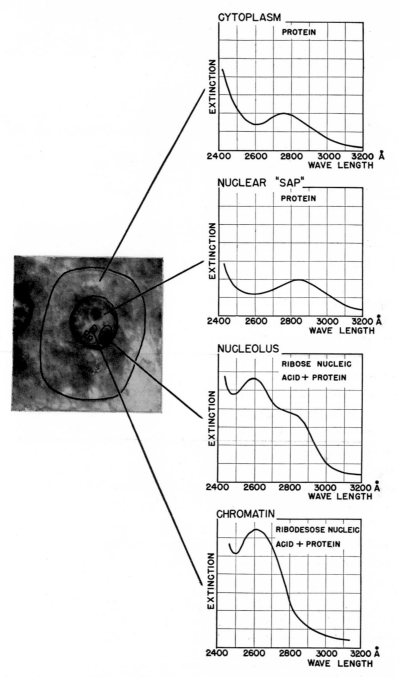

FIGURE 32. A typical not-dividing interphase tissue cell. Diagrams illustrate the usual course of the absorption curves.

usual course. The cytoplasm contains considerable amounts of proteins and sometimes appreciable amounts of nucleotides, especially in the neighborhood of the nuclear membrane (1939, 4; 1942, 2). The nucleus contains proteins and nucleic acids, especially in the chromatin granules. The nucleolar material contains ribose nucleotides and proteins rich in diamino acids (1939, 7, 8, 9; 1940, 2, 6). Because of the small size of mammalian cells it is not profitable on this material to enter into a more thorough study of the chemical distribution of different substances in interphase nuclei.

1. METAPHASE (1940, 3)

Morphologically the most conspicuous phase of the cell division is metaphase. Ultraviolet photographs of living cells from plant and animal material are shown in Figures 24 and 33. The photograph in the center of Figure 33 shows the appearance of grasshopper spermatocytes in metaphase in a fixed preparation. The absorption curves of chromosomes from these cells show them to be very rich in nucleic acids and, furthermore, to contain a protein component. The absorption of the nucleic acids is, however, in these dense structures so very large that even with the highest possible precision in the absorption measurement it is not possible to make an exact determination of the amount or character of the proteins. The data show, however, that in the living cell the sum of the amounts of proteins and nucleic acids often exceeds 40 per cent. In fixed preparations the shrinkage is very great and makes exact estimates of concentration in the living cell impossible. The question of the distribution of the nucleic acid within the chromosome is of some interest for the discussion of its relation to the proteins. Figure 34A shows some curves made with a recording densitometer, across photographs of the chromosome taken at different wave lengths (1936, 1). The curves show a relatively uniform absorption in the central parts of the chromosome. The absorption is highest at the nucleic acid maximum, 2600 Å. If the measurement for that wave length is transformed into extinction coefficient and plotted as ordinate against the chromosome diameter on the horizontal axis, one gets

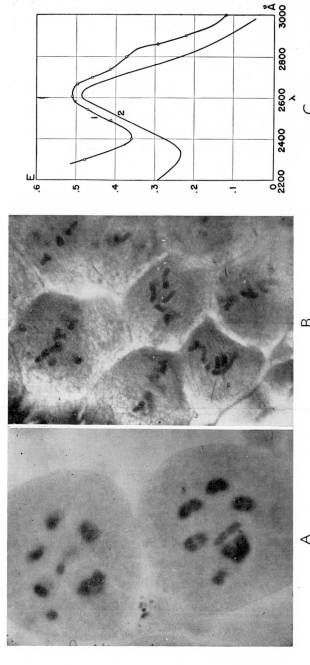

FIGURE 33. A, Living spermatocytes from Myrmus. B, Formalin-fixed spermatocytes from Chorthippus. C (curve 1), Absorption spectrum of central part of metaphase chromosome from Chorthippus. (Curve 2), pure nucleotide absorption.

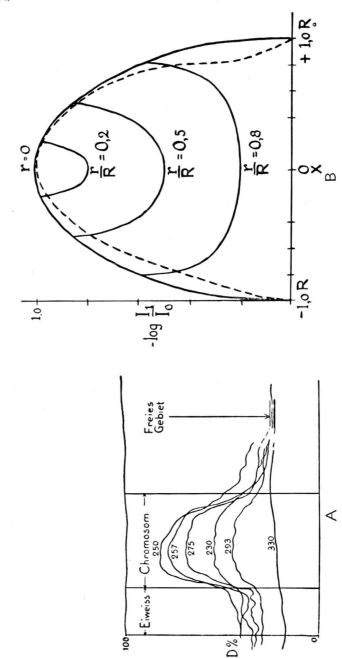

Figure 34. A, Curves made with a recording densitometer, across photographs of a chromosome taken at different wave lengths. B, Solid lines: extinction curves to be expected if a chromosome of the diameter 2R had a non-absorbing core of the diameter 2r. Broken line: calculated extinction curve.

the broken-line curve in Figure 34B (1936, 1). The continuous curves give the absorption which would be theoretically expected for cylinders of absorbing material having central cores of non-absorbing material of various diameters. The curve measured on the chromosome corresponds best to the curve of a cylinder filled with absorbing material, showing that this metaphase chromosome is to be treated as a relatively homogeneous body with approximately even distribution of nucleic acid throughout the whole of its cross section. During the metaphase stage the chromosomes alone represent the total detectable nuclear material. All other nuclear substances have disappeared or cannot be identified in the cell.

2. PROPHASE (1939, 1; 1941, 2)

Figure 35 shows a series of photographs of different prophase stages in the spermatogenesis of a grasshopper (*Gomphocerus*). In this particular, and in our experience rare, case the general arrangement of the nuclear material is so advantageous in optical respects that it is relatively simple to determine the total amount of absorbing material by optical methods and also to get an over-all value of the absorption of the nuclear material. The measurements show a certain increase in nucleic acids during the very earliest prophase. The amount reaches a maximum during the stage which is generally called strepsitene, after which the nucleic acids remain approximately constant until the chromosomes have contracted to typical metaphase shapes. The accuracy in the estimations is not great because of the character of the object. During the course of these two stages one also observes a very conspicuous decrease in the amount of nuclear protein. In the earliest prophase that was measured, the ratio of nucleic acid to protein was approximately 1:20, in late prophase, 1:5, and in metaphase, approximately 1:3. Figure 36 shows in order, beginning at the bottom, the average absorption curves for nuclei in very early prophase, in an intermediate prophase, and in late prophase. They demonstrate the great change in the *ratio* between nucleic acids and proteins during the course of the prophase and the development of the metaphase chromosome.

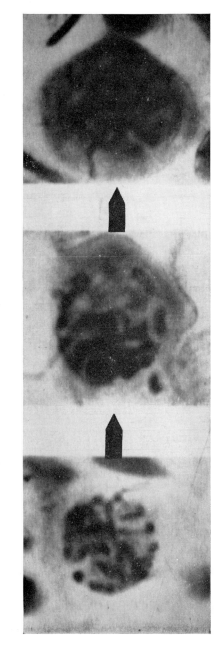

FIGURE 35. Different prophase stages in the spermatogenesis of a grasshopper (*Gomphocerus*).

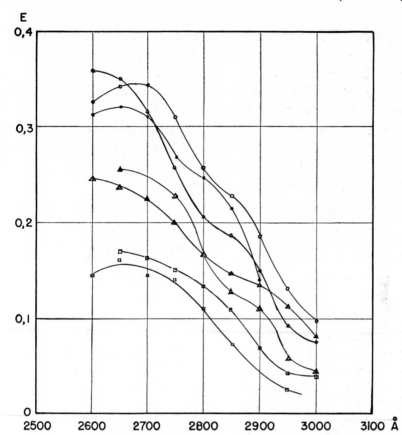

FIGURE 36. Some absorption curves of arbitrarily chosen single points in nuclei, as in Figure 35, in early and intermediate prophase. Earliest cells at the bottom. Without allowing simple quantitative interpretation these curves demonstrate the change in the ratio of nucleic acids to protein.

Chemically the most prominent change during prophase in the nucleus is the disappearance of the major part of the nuclear proteins (cf. 1940, 3). The change in the total amount of nucleic acid during prophase is rather different in different tissues. In some tissues, relatively metabolically inactive and in tissues where divisions occur rapidly, large amounts of nucleic acids persist in dense forms on the chromosome structure during interphase. The change in the amount of protein is, however, always very conspicuous. Even this change seems to be expressed to a different degree in different tissues, which may be an explanation for variation in average sizes of the metaphase chromosomes. One should also note that the speed with which the divisions follow each other seems to influence the extent of this change.

Studies of the nucleic-acid distribution made by nonspectrographic procedures are demonstrated in Figure 37 (1936, 1). There we see photographs of living cells, fixed cells, and cells digested after fixation. The digestion was done with proteolytic enzymes in the presence of lanthanum ions which precipitate the polynucleotides liberated by the digestion (*see* 1935, 1).

3. TELOPHASE (1939, 1; 1940, 3; 1941, 2)

During telophase a development occurs corresponding to the changes during prophase, but in the opposite direction. The metaphasic chromosomes appear to swell, they become surrounded by more and more protein, and they become less and less distinct. During the course of the swelling the chromosomes gradually fill the spaces between them, and the rounded cell nucleus results. As a rule the entire individual chromosomes can no longer be distinguished as separate units. A detailed interpretation of the course of the protein changes during mitosis is not possible without a further analysis of the interphase nucleus. Cell material from metazoa is not suitable for this study because of the small size of the intranuclear structures.

4. INTERPHASE (1940, 3; 1941, 2)

Certain insect cells offer more advantages for such studies. In this group of animals it is common to find giant chromosomes in certain cells. They are the result of endomitotic cell divisions, that is, reproduction of the chromosome material, which is not followed by a division of the cell body. This usually results in highly polyploid cells. In some species, for example Drosophila, we find the curious fact that after division the chromosomes do not separate but remain

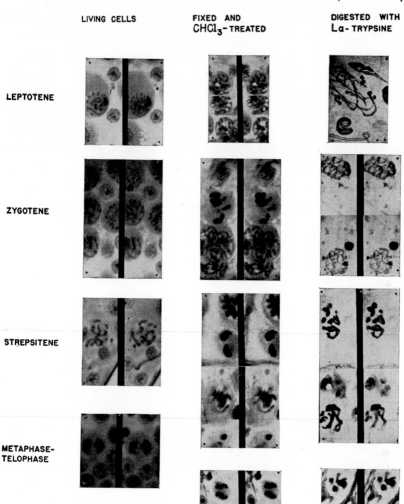

LIVING CELLS   FIXED AND   DIGESTED WITH
                      CHCl₃- TREATED   Lα- TRYPSINE

LEPTOTENE

ZYGOTENE

STREPSITENE

METAPHASE-
TELOPHASE

FIGURE 37. Grasshopper meiosis. Demonstration of ribodesose nucleo-tide component of chromosomes by digestion procedures.

closely paired. After the course of several endomitoses with follow-ing periods of cell growth, we find, instead of the usual high num-ber of small chromosomes, giant chromosomes. The cells perform the activities of usual interphase type, and we have the rare case of a functioning cell in which we can identify different parts of the gene-carrying chromosomes in the interphase. Among these, the so-called "salivary gland chromosomes" of Diptera have been extensively used for various kinds of cytogenetic research, ever since they were first found by Heitz and Bauer and Painter 15 years ago.

Figure 38 shows the appearance of a cell from a Drosophila salivary gland photographed in ultraviolet light. From a central region in the nucleus called the chromocenter (Figure 39), corresponding to the heterochromatin in the metaphase nuclei, a number of chromosome arms with characteristic structure go out. Different places in this ribbonlike structure correspond to the loci of certain genes. Some absorption spectra from different elements in such a nucleus are presented in Figures 40 and 41. It is evident that differ-

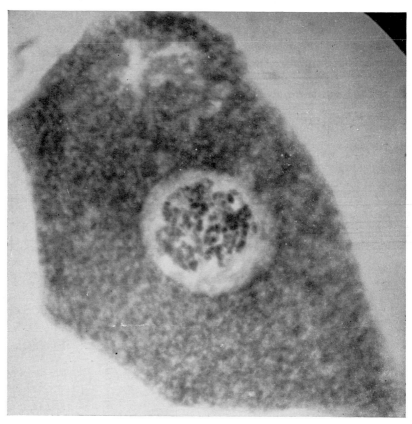

FIGURE 38. Isolated cell from a Drosophila salivary gland.

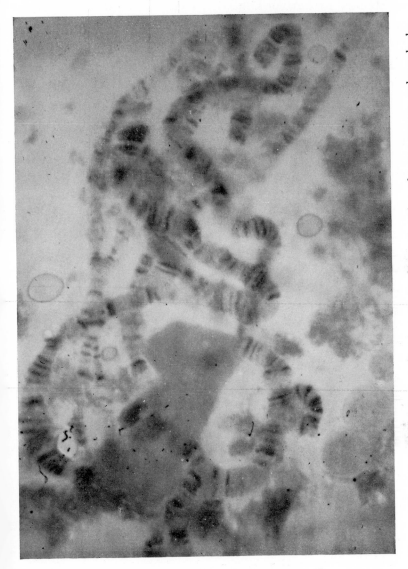

FIGURE 39. Salivary gland nucleus from Drosophila, showing chromocenter and nucleolus. Lens aperture 1,25. Condenser aperture 0,6.

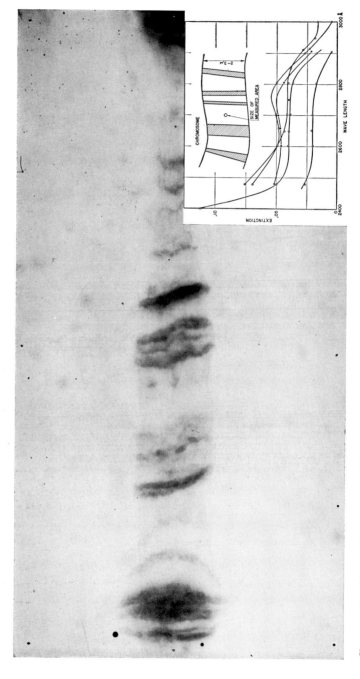

FIGURE 40. Absorption spectra of interband spaces of salivary gland. Lens aperture 1,25. Condenser aperture 0,4.

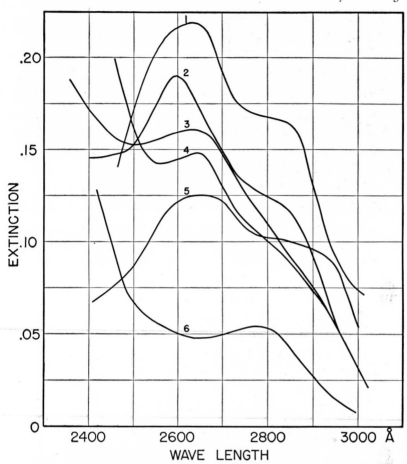

FIGURE 41. Absorption spectra from different parts of a Drosophila salivary gland nucleus: (1) chromocenter, (2) chromosome insertion on
chromocenter, (3 and 4) enchromatic bands, (5) nucleolus, (6) interband
space.

ent parts of the nucleus have quite different compositions with regard to the contents of nucleic acids and proteins. Figure 40 shows
some absorption spectra from interband spaces. They are of interest
because these cell structures are so small that they approach the theoretical limit for the absorption measurements. The absorptions
amount only to a few per cent, and the area measured must not be
larger than a few hundredths of a square micron. The results are,

however, fully reproducible and show that the interband spaces contain proteins with a high content of cyclic amino acids. The nucleolus in the nucleus is situated next to the largest heterochromatic part of the chromatin (Figure 39). The absorption curve of the chromocenter closely resembles that of the nucleolar material. The nucleolar composition (Figure 42) differs in different Drosophila types (1940, 6), but the resemblance of the absorption curves to that of the chromocenter is always present.

According to the microspectrophotometric measurements the salivary gland nucleus is arranged as follows (for details *see* 1940, 3; 1941, 2): From a chromocenter (Figure 43), rich in nucleic acids and in diamino-acid-rich proteins, chromosome arms emerge. These arms show a fine structure of bands rich in nucleic acids interspersed with nucleic-acid-free interband spaces. The nucleic-acid concentration in the band (*see* Figure 45) is high, 10–30 per cent, the exact figure being difficult to determine as even the resolution of the U.V.-microscope does not always reveal the detailed shape of the object. The absolute amount in one band can, however, easily be determined and lies in this material generally between $5–50 \cdot 10^{-11}$ mgs. The bands contain large amounts of proteins in concentrations one to three times that of the interband discs, probably of diamino-acid-rich type as well as of other types in concentrations 10–15 per cent and sometimes above, while the interband spaces contain proteins poorer in diamino acids and in lower concentrations. Because of their stretchability the determination of their volume is even more difficult than for the bands. These proteins contain tyrosine and tryptophane in concentrations of about 5 and 2 per cent, respectively. The heterochromatic regions, intercalated in the chromosomes, and the "puffs" are rich in proteins with a high proportion of diamino acids. The nucleolar proteins also contain large amounts of diamino acids.

During the development of the cell an increase of the chromosome diameter occurs, along with a considerable increase in the chromosome length, the latter mainly conditioned by an increase in the interband space material.

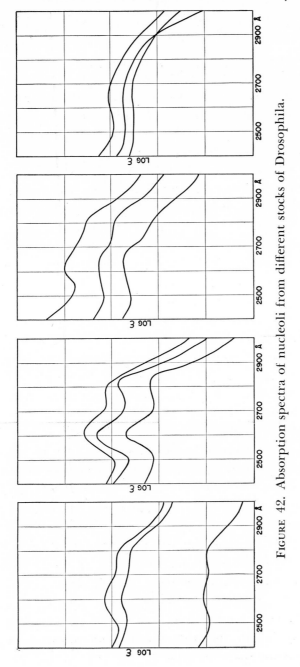

FIGURE 42. Absorption spectra of nucleoli from different stocks of Drosophila.

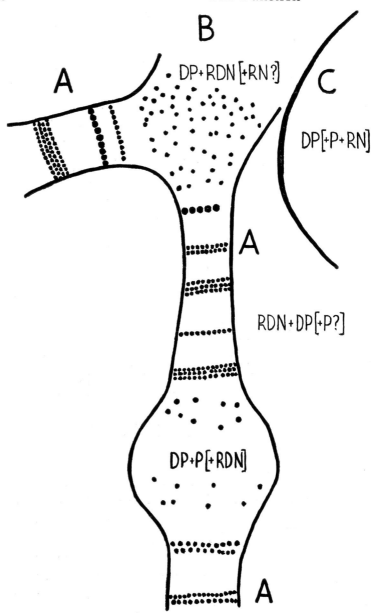

FIGURE 43. Diagram of the chemical composition of the salivary nucleus: A, euchromatin; B, heterochromatin; C, nucleolus; P, protein; DP, diamino-acid-rich protein; RDN, ribodesose nucleotides; RN, ribose nucleotides.

5. COMPARISON BETWEEN THE DIFFERENT MITOTIC STAGES
(FIGURE 44)

The metaphase chromosome contains a chain of linearly arranged genes, packed together into the metaphase chromosome in a spiral fashion. If this metaphase nucleus is compared with the interphase nucleus described above, it would seem that during the transition from metaphase to interphase protein material has accumulated around the gene loci. In this manner the chromosome structures seem to be pressed apart and the tight spirals are relaxed or loosened. In the euchromatic parts this development goes far. In the heterochromatic parts, however, the gene-carrying ele-

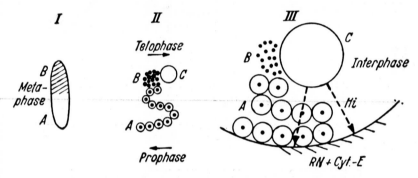

FIGURE 44. Diagram of the protein changes in the nucleus during mitosis: A, euchromatin; B, heterochromatin; C, nucleolus; Cyt-E, cytoplasmic protein; Hi, diamino-acid-rich protein.

ments still lie near each other because a considerable amount of their telophasic products collect in the nucleoli. This development continues, and as a result we find in the interphase a chain containing genes surrounded by primary gene products of protein character. In the heterochromatic regions these products collect into nucleoli, eventually located around the nucleolus-organizing regions, if such are developed. This development corresponds closely to what was assumed above for the case of the metazoan cells (1940, 3).

Observations on different cell materials show that this telephasic

breakdown of proteins and partial disappearance of ribose nucleotides from the nucleus proceeds to different degrees in different
tissues, resulting in metaphase chromosomes of different sizes. In
metabolically active tissues this development goes far, but in metabolically less active tissues it is often possible to follow the
metaphasic arrangement of the nuclear material around individual
chromosomes in interphase. (For details about the changes during
mitosis, *see* 1940, 3; 1941, 2.)

Finally it should be mentioned that it is not possible to differen-
tiate between ribodesose and ribose nucleotides by absorption
measurements. In the metaphase chromosome the Feulgen reaction shows that at least a very large part of the chromosome nucleic
acid is of ribodesose type. During prophase and interphase one can,
however, often observe considerable amounts of ribose nucleic acid
in those structures which are homologous to parts of the metaphase
chromosome. This is especially conspicuous in metabolically active
cells. These ribose nucleic acids may be correlated with the production of the proteins, described above as primary gene products.
It is also possible that they may appear in the metaphase chromosome.

6. NUCLEIC ACIDS AND GENE REPRODUCTION

As mentioned above, it has been shown that the quantity of
nucleic acid in the grasshopper spermatocyte chromosomes is max-
imal during cell division (1939, 1). This needs further investigation but points with some probability towards a connection between the duplication of the genes and the presence of nucleic acid.
Further and more solid support for this view has been provided by
cytochemical studies on variegated races of Drosophila carried
through by Schultz and the author (1938, 2; 1939, 4, 7, 8, 9, 10; 1940,
6). Schultz has found earlier that in some of these races visible
changes in phenotype could be correlated with certain chromosome derangements which must have been due to disturbances in
the reproduction of certain genes in certain cells. Closer study
of the salivary chromosomes at the points where the genes in ques-

tion are situated revealed severe disturbances in the metabolism
of nucleic acids.

One of the ways in which these studies were carried out by
Schultz and the author is exemplified by Figures 45 and 46. The
figures show the X-chromosome pair of the type of Drosophila female studied. One chromosome partner is normal while the other
is involved in a translocation with the fourth chromosome, such
that the latter is broken in a heterochromatic region. This female
would be phenotypically variegated for genes lying in the part of
the broken X-chromosome that has been juxtaposed to lie near
the heterochromatin of the fourth chromosome (Schultz). When
the amount of nucleic acid in the individual bands was measured it
was shown that the nucleic-acid synthesis was disturbed in those
bands carrying the variegating genes. It was further shown that
there exists a close correlation between the extent of disturbance
in the gene reproduction and the extent of disturbance in the

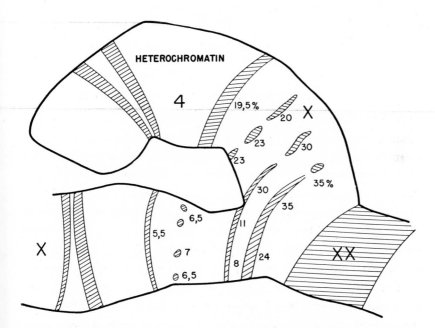

FIGURE 45. Determinations of amount of nucleic acid of individual
bands in Drosophila translocations, figures in per cent.

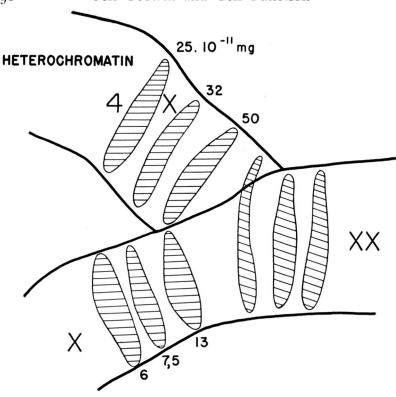

FIGURE 46. Drosophila translocation. Numbers give total amount nucleotides per band.

nucleotide metabolism. This observation led to the conclusion that *nucleic acids are necessary prerequisites for the reproduction of genes (1938, 2) and that they are probably necessary for the multiplication of self-reproducing protein molecules in general.*

Moreover, from the results of investigations on different Drosophila material, it could be concluded that the heterochromatin (specially studied by Schultz, 1939, 10), far from being inert, is a regulating center for the nucleic acid metabolism of the chromosome as well as that of the cytoplasm (1939, 2, 3, 4, 7, 8, 9). It was possible to show that changes in the heterochromatin could result in changes in the nucleotide and protein metabolism in the other chromosomes of the nucleus as well as in the same chromosome.

Furthermore, the heterochromatin influences the composition of the nucleolus. Also the protein and nucleic-acid metabolism of the cytoplasm was influenced by the amount of heterochromatin in the nucleus. Thus it is evident that we have in heterochromatin a very important system for the regulation of nucleic-acid metabolism.

7. SURVEY OF PROTEIN CHANGES DURING THE MITOTIC CYCLE

(1) If the cytochemical data from different stages of the cell cycle are put together, using the salivary gland nucleus as a type for an interphase nucleus, the outline in Figure 44 results. During the telophasic development from metaphase to interphase the euchromatic regions of a chromosome produce protein with absorption type of the tyrosine- and tryptophane-rich protein, and the heterochromatic regions produce proteins rich in diamino acids. The products of the latter regions collect to the nucleolus, the function of which is correlated with the synthesis of cytoplasmic protein, as will be described later. During the development from interphase to metaphase the major part of the protein is broken down and nucleic acids are concentrated on the chromosome. The chromosome contracts with spiralization—a phenomenon which might be caused by small differences in the spacing of the nucleotide and polypeptide chains.

(2) Ribodesose nucleic acid participates in the gene protein reproduction. The possibility that the ribose nucleic acids also play a part therein cannot at present be excluded.

During the period of the production of what is described above as primary gene products both ribodesose and ribose nucleic acids have been found in the nucleus.

(3) Heterochromatin directs the nucleic-acid metabolism and thus the protein metabolism in the other chromosomes of the nucleus, the nucleolus, and the cytoplasm as well as in the chromosome in which it lies.

The general conclusions that ribodesose nucleic acid is necessary for gene reproduction and that the heterochromatic regions of the chromosomes influence the chromosome nucleic-acid metabolism seem to have wider implications. Comparisons with other intracellular self-reproducing proteins, such as viruses and phages, led to the general idea expressed by Schultz and the author (1938, 2) that all self-reproducing protein molecules need the co-operation of nucleic acids for reproduction. That view has been supported by subsequent work and has also gained further strength from the observation presented in the next chapter to the effect that the production of cytoplasmic protein also needs the co-operation of nucleotides.

CHAPTER V

The organization of the system for cytoplasmic protein formation in the normal metazoan cell

As YET ONLY the production of the proteins in the cell nucleus has been described, and that with special regard to the production of gene proteins in connection with nucleic-acid metabolism. Those proteins appeared around the gene loci, while the nuclear development proceeded from metaphase to functional interphase.

Between the mitotic cycles lies that period of cell life during which the cell grows to its definite size and carries out its special function in the organism. During growth a very large increase in the total mass of protein occurs in the cell, in most cases quantitatively far larger than the increase due to the process of production of new genes during the last division. The main masses of the newly formed protein substances are either found in the cytoplasm or are secreted out of the cell.

The mechanism for cytoplasmic protein formation has been studied in a number of different cell materials, and, in order to simplify the presentation, I will first present a diagram showing the organization of the cytoplasmic protein-forming system.

The general results are given in outline in Figure 47 (1941, 2, 7; 1942, 2). This figure represents a cell in intense production of cytoplasmic proteins. In that cell the following system is working: a certain part of the chromatin (in the figure marked A), called the *nucleolus-associated chromatin,* produces substances of protein nature. There are indications that these substances contain con-

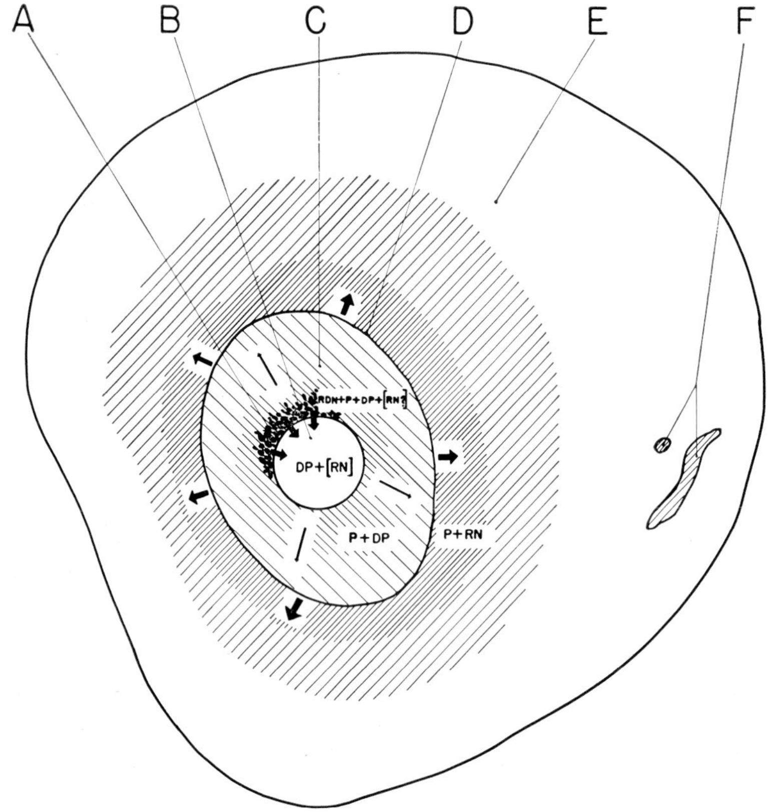

FIGURE 47. Diagram of the main endocellular system for cytoplasmic protein formation in intense function. A, nucleolus-associated chromatin; B, nucleolus; C, nucleus; D, nuclear membrane; E, cytoplasm; F, separate nucleotide-containing systems in cytoplasm. RDN, ribodesose nucleotides; RN, ribose nucleotides; P, proteins; DP, diamino-acid-rich proteins. Brackets mean smaller and varying quantities.

siderable amounts of diamino acids. They accumulate and form the main bulk of a large nucleolus, B. From the nucleolus they diffuse towards the nuclear membrane, D, on the outside of which an intensive production of ribose nucleotides takes place. At the same time, the amount of cytoplasmic proteins increases. The gradient in concentration indicating the diffusion within the nucleus is represented in the diagram by the arrows marked in C. The gradient in the cytoplasm in the concentration of nucleotides, falling from the nucleolar membrane towards the wall of the cell, is indicated in the cytoplasm, E. Different series of investigations (1940, 2, 3, 6; 1941, 2, 10; 1942, 2) show the special character of the nucleolus-associated chromatin, the composition of the nucleolus, and a very close relationship between the chromatin in question and nucleolar substances. Furthermore, the gradients in concentration of protein and nucleotides, respectively, from the nucleolus to the nuclear membrane and from the latter towards the cell membrane, have been established (1939, 3, 7; 1941, 2; 1943, 5). There is also other evidence of a more complicated kind for the former protein transport (1943, 2). The increase in cytoplasmic ribose nucleic acid during the protein synthesis is conspicuously shown in every case of protein increase (cf. below).

Cells of various origin engaged in intense production of cytoplasmic proteins are remarkably alike when studied in ultraviolet light. Especially conspicuous in the ultraviolet photographs are, thanks to the chemical changes in the organelles concerned in the process, in all cases the large nucleoli, which stand out strongly in ultraviolet light because of their high protein content and sometimes fairly high amounts of ribose nucleotides, and also the dark, nucleic-acid-rich cytoplasm.

Figure 48 demonstrates the development of the nucleolus in a cell which starts growing rapidly (1941, 10; 1944, 4; 1948, 4). The cell to the left is not growing, but when growth starts nucleolar material appears inside the chromocenter which is pressed aside and "exploded" by the nucleolar substances. *The main chromocenter now appears as the main nucleolus-associated chromatin.* At the same time ribose nucleic acids appear around the nucleolar membrane and diffuse out into the cytoplasm. Figure 49 shows this development in a cell, which because of its size is very suitable, namely the neurocyte during its development from early neuroblast (1943, 5).

A remarkable feature in the nucleolar substances is their very high content of proteins. The denseness of the structure often

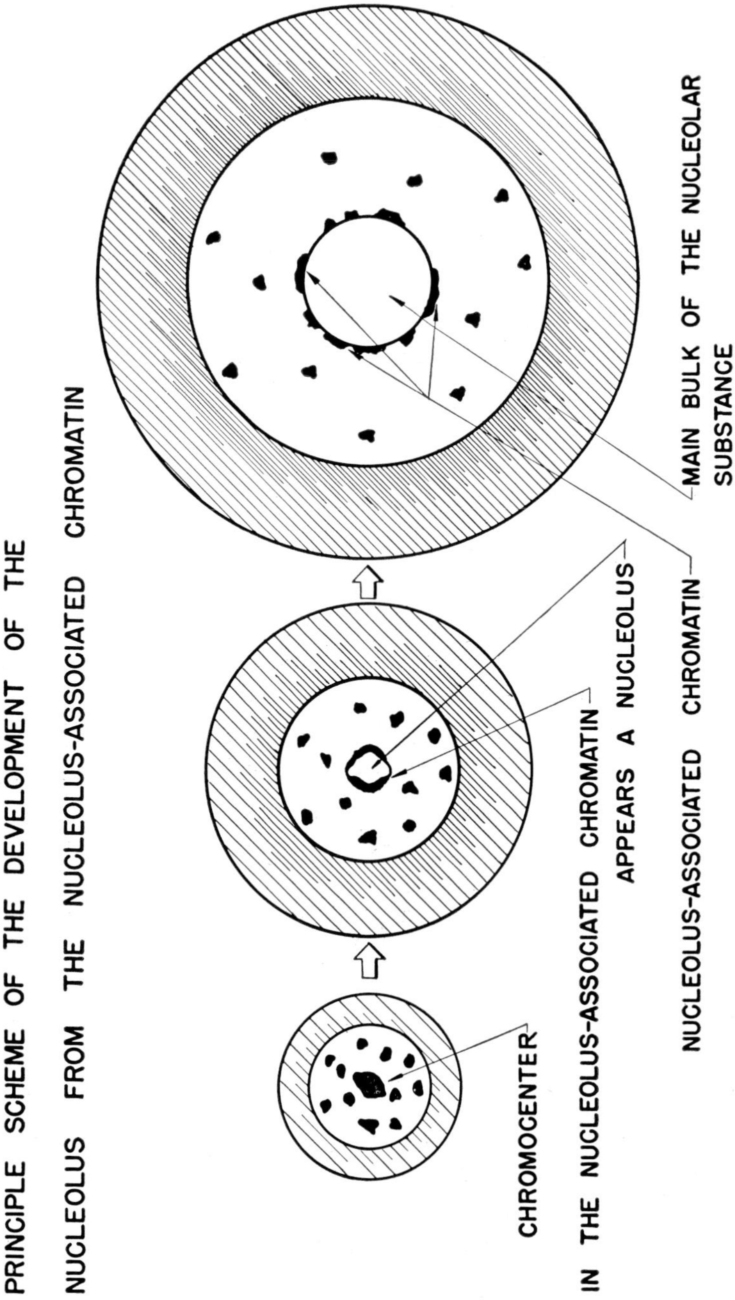

PRINCIPLE SCHEME OF THE DEVELOPMENT OF THE

NUCLEOLUS FROM THE NUCLEOLUS-ASSOCIATED CHROMATIN

MAIN BULK OF THE NUCLEOLAR
SUBSTANCE

NUCLEOLUS-ASSOCIATED CHROMATIN

APPEARS A NUCLEOLUS

NUCLEOLUS-ASSOCIATED CHROMATIN

IN THE NUCLEOLUS-ASSOCIATED CHROMATIN

CHROMOGENTER

FIGURE 48. Diagram of development of nucleolus from nucleolus-associated chromatin.

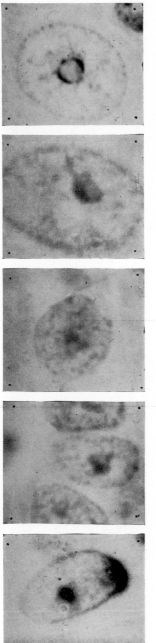

FIGURE 49. Photographs of development of nucleolus inside the nucleolus-associated chromatin.

makes precise determination of absolute amounts difficult. The favorable optical homogeneity of the structures is, however, of great advantage. Protein contents above 20 per cent have been a rule in the material investigated and in individual cases up to over 40 per cent have been observed in the frozen-dried preparations. Most nucleoli contain also ribose nucleotides in low concentrations compared with the proteins (1939, 7, 8, 9, 10; 1940, 3, 6; 1941, 5). The nucleotide content varies very much and nucleotides may even be absent.

The central rôle of the nucleolus-associated chromatin and the nucleolus in the cytoplasmic protein synthesis makes it especially important to investigate their general interactions. The Chironomus salivary chromosomes are very useful for this investigation. Dr. Hans Bauer and the author have lately studied the formation of nucleolar substances in that form, and it was possible to demonstrate that they were synthesized within certain restricted parts of the chromosomes (1948, 1). They either appeared as a swelling of a part of the chromosome or were collected both inside and around the corresponding chromosome section (Figure 50).

Some nerve cells, because of their immense size, offer a good opportunity to study the transport of material from the nucleolus towards the nuclear membrane. As Hydén has shown by his analysis of the so-called "Chromatinaustrittbilder" in certain fish ganglion cells (1943, 2), this process is not an extrusion of chromatin from the nucleus but an extremely intense activity of the system for cytoplasmic protein formation, as shown in the diagram in Figure 47. Because of the very high level of new formation of proteins, the nucleus is pushed away towards the side of the cell and the main functional activity is thus concentrated on one side of the nucleus.

The increase of nucleolar masses is a most conspicuous phenomenon during cytoplasmic protein synthesis. During periods of intensive growth, the nucleolus increases, sometimes enormously, and contains both ribose nucleotides and proteins rich in diamino acids. In cells which do not form any cytoplasmic protein the nucleoli are very small or apparently absent. Exceptions have been

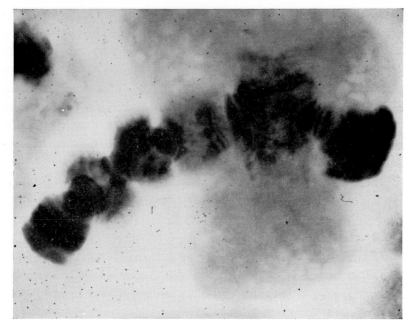

A

B

FIGURE 50. Photographs of nucleolus-forming regions of Chironomus chromosome, demonstrating the appearance of nucleolar substances inside the chromosome at a certain defined locus. The substances collect also around the chromosome strands.

found, but only in cells which are prepared for a period of very rapid growth, as in parts of the dormant plant embryo. Nucleolar material is absent during mitosis, when no cell growth occurs. In the morphological literature only a few other cell types are described as being without nucleolar material. The classical type is the spermatocyte. This is probably the only cell in the organism in which a direct decomposition of cytoplasmic masses occurs during the course of cell differentiation—which explains the absence of such material. Another type is indicated by certain cells which are the end result of a long chain of differentiation and never grow or divide, for instance the leucocytes of mammals. A third type of some interest in this connection is found in many early embryonic cells. In certain Echinoderm eggs, for example, no visible nucleoli appear until the gastrula stage, but in these cases, also, there is no increase in the total amount of proteins in the embryo until that stage. Soon after gastrulation the larva starts to feed, growth begins, and immediately nucleoli appear.

In certain other yolk-rich eggs nucleoli appear earlier, which is interpreted as cellular metabolic processes of the kind described. It is important that the case described above, which was theoretically expected, is actually found in certain objects.

The appearance of ribose nucleotides in the cytoplasm during the protein synthesis is a phenomenon which is easily seen by means of the simple ultraviolet microscope. As a number of examples are given later, the reader is referred to the following paragraphs.

The definition of the word *nucleolus* is not precise in cytological literature. The term, as used in the literature, often covers material here described as nucleolus-associated chromatin and as other endonuclear structures. In the older literature, larger heterochromatic parts of the chromatin are also included. For cytochemical work an exact definition is badly needed. Since the structure referred to in these studies by that name is well defined and easily identified in all cells studied, the following definition seems suitable: *Nucleoli are dense, rounded, as a rule optically homogeneous, endonuclear bodies consisting of proteins in high concentrations, rich in diamino acids and associated with the cytoplasmic pro-*

tein formation. Often they contain some ribose nucleotides, but never ribodesose nucleotides (rarely small granular inclusions which probably are of chromatic character may occur). The nucleoli are intimately connected both spatially and chemically with the nucleolus-associated chromosome regions or the nucleolus-organizing region, when such is developed.

It is, of course, premature to conclude that the material defined in this way was not connected with other synthetic processes than those leading to the formation of cytoplasmic proteins. In all materials investigated it is, however, evident that the appearance of nucleolar substances follows so closely the rate of the protein synthesis that it seems reasonable to assume that the quantitatively dominating part thereof is connected with that process. In order to study that question further, different materials have been studied among which the Chironomus material should be mentioned (1948, 1). On different loci in the salivary gland, masses of substances appear in the same way as does the main nucleolus. There are no nucleolus organizers in this object. That might mean that "nucleolar" substances are merely primary products of the gene activity in general and that the reason why those substances connected with the cytoplasmic protein synthesis appear as conspicuous nucleolar bodies is simply their relatively enormous size, conditioned by the comprehensiveness of the chemical processes in which they are linked.

The intracellular system for protein formation described in Figure 47 operates during different types of cell activity, both those connected with growth processes and those connected with the specific function of the cell in the organism. In later chapters some examples will be given.

1. ORGANIZATON DURING GROWTH

We shall consider examples of the three most important types of growth in normal mammalian tissues, namely, embryonal growth, growth in the adult organism, and cell regeneration.

The embryonal growth (1939, 4; 1941, 2, 10) progresses with very great speed, especially during the earliest stages of embryonic development.

Our examples are from the chick embryo. Between the second and tenth day of incubation, an enormous growth occurs and the embryo increases more than twenty times in weight. In all tissues the cells show signs of intense function of the system for protein formation in the cytoplasm. Figure 51 shows liver from a chick embryo on the third day, the time when the growth is most rapid. The tissue has enormous nucleoli and very high concentrations of ribose nucleotides in the cytoplasm. The upper curves give absorp-

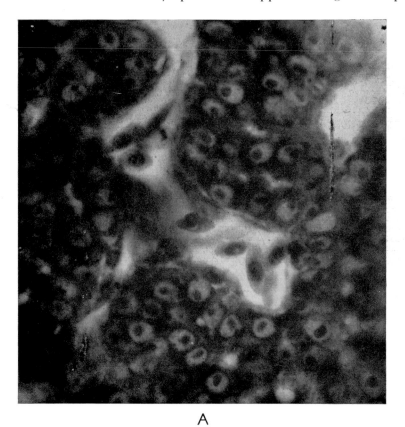

A

FIGURE 51. Early embryonic liver cells during most rapid growth. A, Ultraviolet photograph.

tion data from 5μ sections of the cytoplasm of embryonic liver cells showing an enormous nucleotide absorption, corresponding to a nucleic-acid content of about 3 per cent of the wet weight. Corresponding measurements on adult liver (lower curves) show considerable concentrations of nucleotides but not over a tenth of that found in the rapidly growing cells. Ultramicro determinations of phosphorus, according to Norberg, support the evidence of the ultraviolet work (1942, 4).

Figure 52 shows the difference between embryonic blood cells (A) and adult cells (B) (1941, 10). The corresponding absorption spectra of points in the cytoplasm show a very high nucleotide ab-

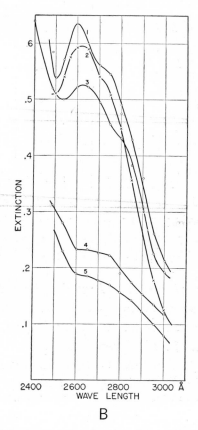

B

B (curves 1, 2 and 3), from points in cytoplasm of cells as in A. Curves 4 and 5, from liver cells of newly hatched chicken.

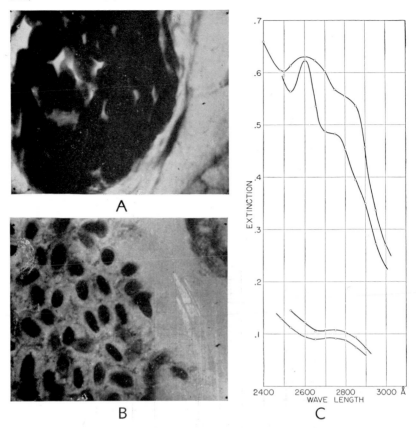

FIGURE 52. A, Embryonic blood corpuscles (*Area vasculosa* of chick embryo), cytoplasms quite dark. B, Blood corpuscles from hen, cytoplasms with very low absorption. C, Corresponding absorption curves.

sorption in the cytoplasms of embryonic cells and practically no nucleic acid absorption in that of the adult cells. The following figure (Figure 53) demonstrates the same thing in the kidney: (left) embryonic and (right) adult tissue.

The conditions are the same in the plant embryo (1939, 4).

In the adult animal organism, growth occurs normally in some tissues as, for example, during the production of new egg cells in the ovary. Figure 54 demonstrates the high content of nucleotides in the cytoplasm of the egg nurse cells of an adult Drosophila fe-

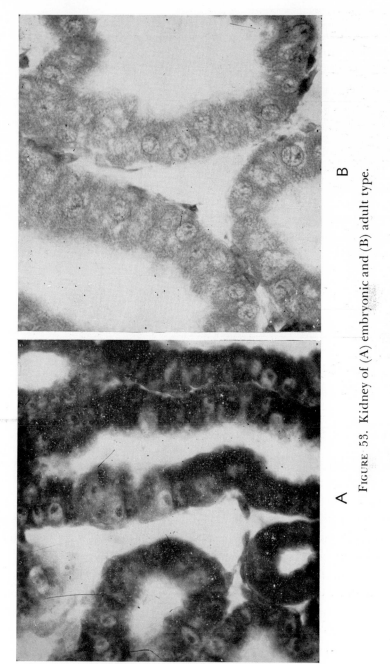

A   B

FIGURE 53. Kidney of (A) embryonic and (B) adult type.

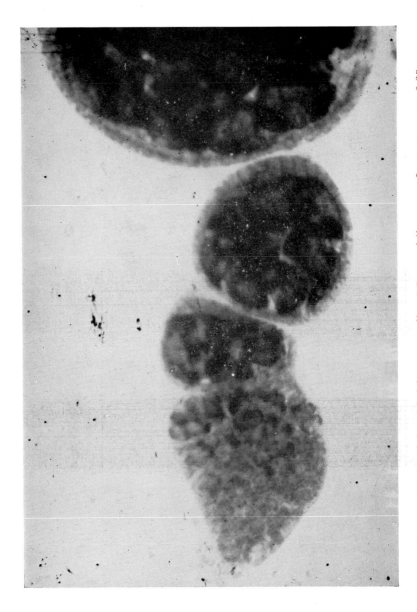

FIGURE 54. Nucleic-acid-rich nurse cells of Drosophila ovary. Lens aperture 0,35.

male (1939, 7, 8). In the adult plant organism rapid growth occurs in various tissues. In Figure 55 the high content of ribose nucleotides shows up as a great absorption in the cytoplasm in the growth zone of the Allium root (1939, 4). If growing and mature cells are isolated and mixed together for comparison under identical conditions one can get photographs such as those in Figure 55 A. The dark cells are from the growth zone and show a very high nucleotide absorption at 2600 Å. (Figure 56). The light cells from a zone of no growth show an absorption curve following that of proteins in general. How well Norberg's ultramicro determinations of nucleic-acid phosphates on this material corroborate the absorption data seen in Figure 57 (1942, 4).

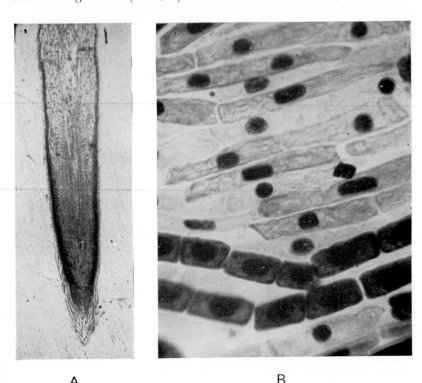

A   B

FIGURE 55. A, Root tip of Allium, indicating generally higher amounts of absorbing substances in growth zone than in mature zones. Lens aperture 0,15. B, isolation preparation of cells from both zones.

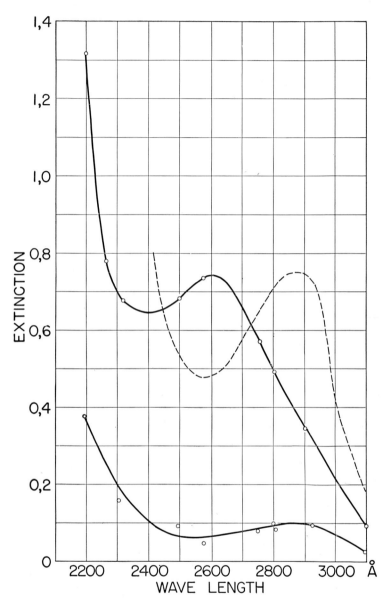

FIGURE 56. Absorption spectrum from cell cytoplasms from both zones in Figure 55, showing a great difference in protein amount per cell and a still more conspicuous difference in ribose nucleotide content. Broken curve is the result of the lower curve multiplied by an arbitrary factor in order to illustrate the difference in general course of the absorption.

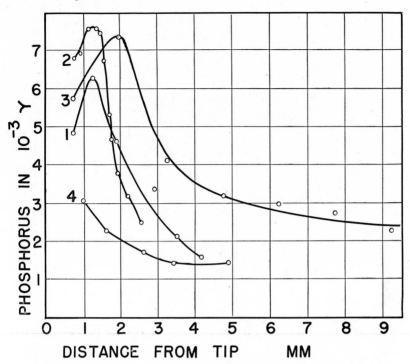

FIGURE 57. Phosphorus content in 1μ cuts from root of *Allium cepa* determined according to Norberg. Curve 1, Total phosphorus. Curve 2, Nucleotide absorption in an arbitrary scale from ultraviolet measurements cited above. The steeper decrease in the absorption curve as compared with the phosphorus curve is artificial owing to the measuring technique. Curve 3, Total phosphorus. Curve 4, Residual phosphorus in another experiment.

The third type of growth to be considered is regeneration. Figure 58 is taken from work done by Stowell in Stockholm and demonstrates how the system for protein formation starts to work after excision of parts of liver (1948, 10). In the normal liver there are small nucleoli and low concentrations of nucleotides in the cytoplasm. In regeneration after partial hepatectomy the nucleoli start growing and become rich in ribose nucleotides which also appear around the nuclear membrane.

The fact that the organelles of the system for cytoplasmic protein

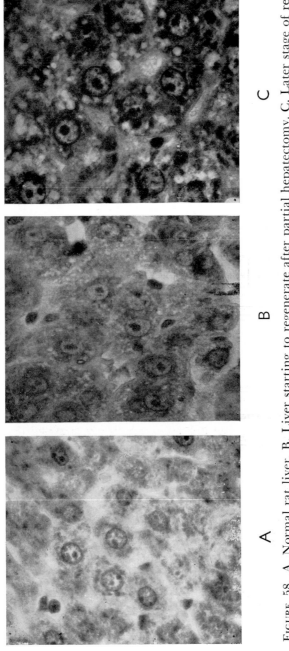

FIGURE 58. A, Normal rat liver. B, Liver starting to regenerate after partial hepatectomy. C, Later stage of regeneration (Stowell).

ormation are well developed does not necessarily mean that the
cell is at the moment in a state of rapid protein formation. It may
mean that it is in a state of readiness for rapid protein forma-
ion. In rare cases one finds cells with large nucleoli and heavily
ultraviolet-absorbing cytoplasm, which are not growing but which
will start growing immediately, when the proper stimulus reaches
them (1939, 9). One example is the plant seed before germination.
Another example is found in the imaginal discs of Drosophila where
Schultz and the author found that the cells have the appearance
shown in Figure 59, quite different from the other cells of the larva.

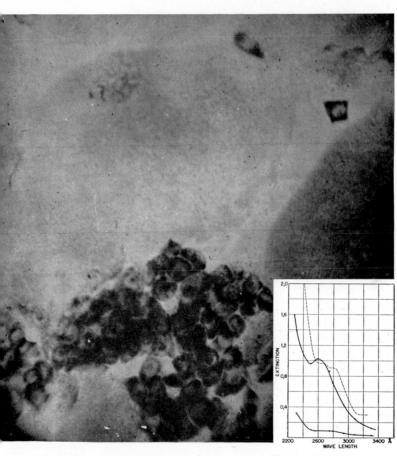

FIGURE 59. Imaginal disc cells and larval cells from Drosophila. Curves
arranged as in Figure 56.

These cells will start growing with very great speed at pupation and will form imaginal tissues. As was shown in a previous chapter, the entire system for protein formation of the cytoplasm is regulated by nuclear genes, probably mainly situated in the euchromatin.

2. ORGANIZATION DURING CELL FUNCTION OF VARIOUS KINDS

A. GLANDS

In the metazoan tissues the function of some cells is combined with very intense protein metabolic processes. Most prominent are probably those in the cells whose task it is to produce protein-rich secretions (1941, 8). Figure 60 shows ultraviolet photographs from a rabbit pancreas, where a cell can produce its own weight in protein in less than 24 hours. The nucleoli and the cytoplasmic nucleotides are conspicuous. When the pancreas is discharged by aid of pilocarpine, a very great decrease in cell protein occurs and then a rapid restitution and rapid new synthesis of protein sets in, preceded by

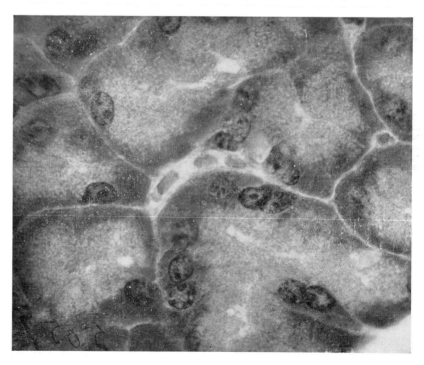

FIGURE 60. Rabbit pancreas cells.

the nucleolar growth and the appearance of large nucleotide rings around the nuclear membranes, as presented in Figure 47 (Figure 61; 1941, 8, p. 116–18). The islands of Langerhans give a nice opportunity to compare tissues producing protein rapidly with tissues

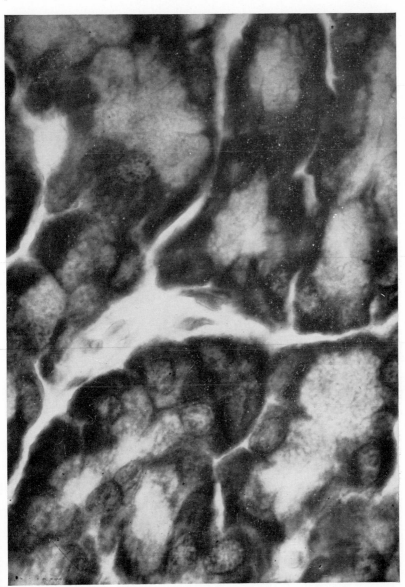

FIGURE 61. Rabbit pancreas, restitution after pilocarpine stimulation.

producing protein slowly in the same preparation (Figure 62). The islands themselves produce insulin—and the total amount of protein produced by them in a given time is very much less than that produced by the exocrine cells in the same time. As is to be expected, the measurements show that the concentration of cytoplasmic nucleotides is much higher in the cytoplasm of the exocrine

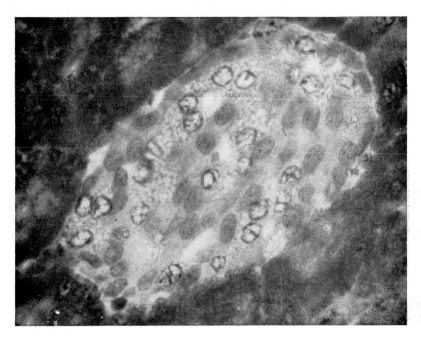

FIGURE 62. Island of Langerhans, great difference in absorption at 2570 Å. between exocrine and endocrine part.

part than in that of the endocrine part (1941, 8, p. 120). Nucleotide determinations, according to Norberg, match the spectrophotometric data very well (1942, 4).

Another example of the same kind is furnished by the gastric mucosa. Here we have two cell types mixed together, one of which produces hydrochloric acid while the other produces a protein-rich secretion. In the ultraviolet microscope at the absorption maximum of the nucleotides the mucosa looks like a mosaic of heavily absorbing protein-producing cells and relatively clear hydrochloric-acid producing cells (Figure 63). The former contain considerably more proteins than the latter, on an average more than twice the amount (1941, 8, p. 124), but the main difference in the photograph is conditioned by ribose nucleotides, of which the former have on an average three to four times the amount of the latter.

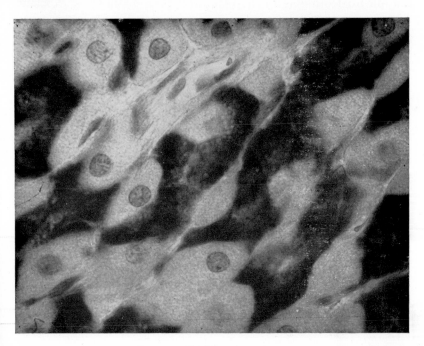

FIGURE 63. Gastric mucosa.

The salivary gland of Drosophila larvae gives us an opportunity for a closer study of the quantitative procedures correlated with growth and function (1939, 7, 8, 9). The individual cells can easily be separated, and a large series of absorption spectra from points in the cytoplasm showed that all curves from cells in one gland had the same shape, that is, a certain ratio between nucleotides and proteins. This ratio changes during cell development. Figure 64 demonstrates the method for determination of the "total extinctions" of individual cells, squeezed between coverslip and slide but unbroken. By total extinction at a wave length is meant the average

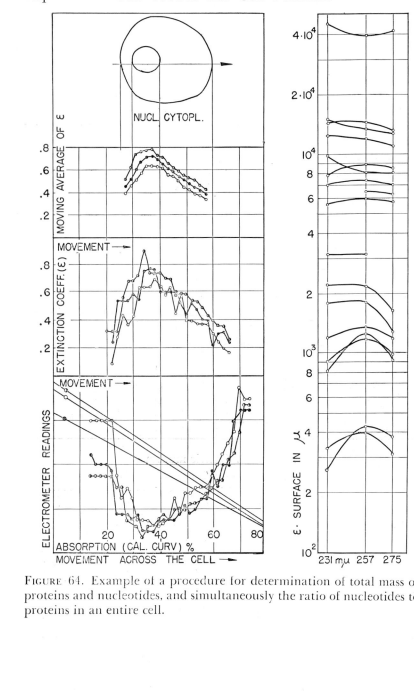

FIGURE 64. Example of a procedure for determination of total mass of proteins and nucleotides, and simultaneously the ratio of nucleotides to proteins in an entire cell.

decadic extinction of an area multiplied by that area, in this case the optical cross section of the cell. This value is independent of the degree of pressing of an individual cell. As representative of the average extinction coefficient of a cell, the average has been taken along one diameter. In the left series of diagrams the top one represents the cell and the one at the bottom a series of photocell measurements taken across the cell, marked as electrometer readings. These data can be transferred into per cents by aid of a rotating step-sector, the calibration curves of which are presented as straight lines in the diagram. Of the two diagrams in the middle, the lower one gives the extinctions calculated this way and the one above shows the curve smoothed out by a moving average of three points. The total extinction of the whole cell is then calculated by multiplying each extinction coefficient by the area of the cell for which it is representative (a ring-shaped area). In the diagram on the right in Figure 64 are plotted the results of such a series of determinations of total amounts of absorbing substances in gland cells of different ages. The youngest cells are smallest and at the bottom of the diagram; the size and age increase upwards. The amounts are plotted in a logarithmic scale. It is evident that in the young cells the nucleic-acid absorption dominates the picture, but in older cells, which in this case are more than a hundred times larger than the youngest measured, the nucleotide absorption is inconspicuous compared with that of the protein. The nucleic acids increase also, and the ratio of nucleic-acid amount per cell to protein amount is largest at the earliest stages when the speed of growth is largest (Schultz and Caspersson, 1939).

B. HEMATOPOIESIS

The hematopoietic system has been studied especially by Thorell (1944, 2; 1945, 2, 4; 1947, 17, 18, 19; 1948, 5, 6). The bone marrow is an excellent material for cytochemical techniques as the cells can be studied and measured in the living state.

In Figure 65 (from Thorell 1947, 17) are shown the cytochemical changes occurring during the formation of white blood cells. During the development from the myeloblast to the definite granulocyte, the increase in cytoplasmic proteins occurs almost exclusively at the stage between myeloblast and promyelocyte. During that particular period the cytoplasmic ribose nucleic-acid content and the volume of the nucleolus are both very high. At later stages no appreciable formation of new proteins occurs and cytoplasmic nucleotides and nucleolar volume decrease rapidly.

When it was shown by Thorell that in the blood cell in general the protein-forming system worked according to the diagram in Figure 47, it was possible to turn the problem around and *to determine the state of growth or function of the individual cell from the analysis of the state of function of the system for cytoplasmic protein formation.* Several different questions of hematological interest have been studied by Thorell along these lines, for which the reader is referred to the original papers.

C. THE NERVE CELL

Another interesting example is the nerve cell. This cell confused us no end in the beginning. The cytochemical measurements (1941, 5) showed, for example, that the Nissl bodies contain large numbers of ribose nucleotides, and a closer analysis showed the cell to correspond to the general organization of a cell engaged in rapid protein synthesis, as in Figure 47. Its organization resembles that of the egg cell, and one can take the egg cell in its second period of growth as being the most typical example of rapidly growing cells. Thus it is to be expected that this type of cell is either carrying out, or ready to carry out, a rapid protein synthesis even in the adult organism (cf. above). There were, however, in the literature no data on protein changes in the nerve cell. As this cell seemed to be an exception to the rule, a very careful study was started by Hydén.

At first, he studied the embryonic development (1942, 3; 1943, 5). The early stages correspond to those of embryonic cells in general, with regard to the system for cytoplasmic protein formation. Towards the end of the embryonic development, however, the cell continues to keep the organelles of the system for protein forma-

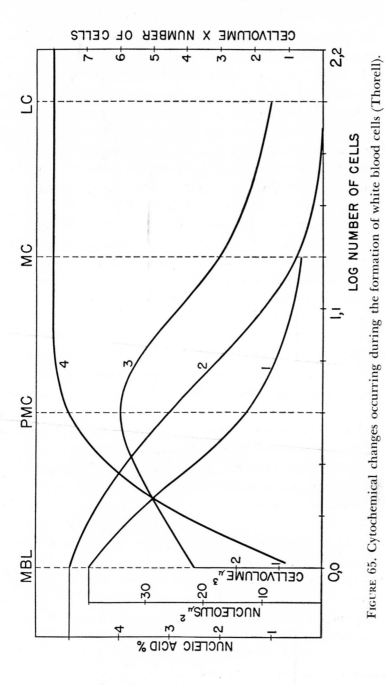

FIGURE 65. Cytochemical changes occurring during the formation of white blood cells (Thorell).

127

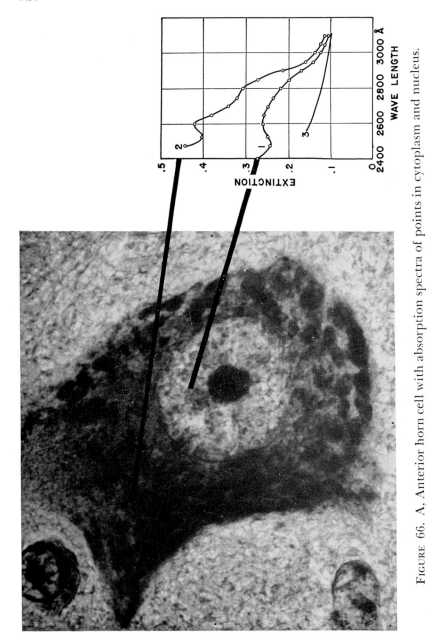

FIGURE 66. A, Anterior horn cell with absorption spectra of points in cytoplasm and nucleus.

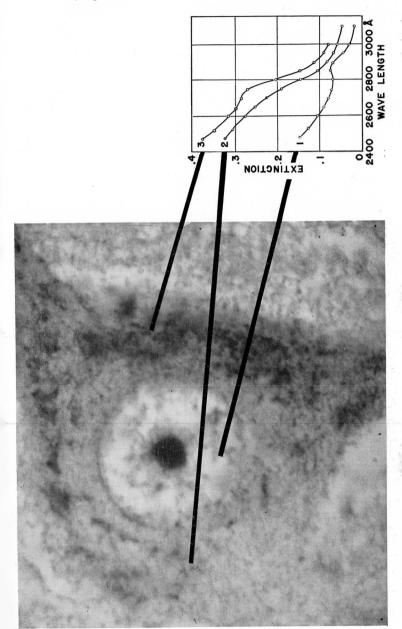

B, Similar cell after heavy muscular work showing great decrease in cytoplasmic protein masses and also in cytoplasmic nucleotides (Hydén 1943, 5).

tion of the cytoplasm in a state corresponding to intense activity. It goes through a period of intense growth which can be compared with the second period of growth of the egg cell, during which it reaches its definite size. Even after that, however, the nerve cell keeps the characteristics indicating intense protein formation. As it seemed possible that this phenomenon could be connected with the ordinary function of the cell, Hydén started studies in which animals were forced to perform heavy muscular work. He also tried sensory stimulation (1943, 5; 1944, 3; 1945, 3; 1947, 6, 7, 8). In both cases during exhaustive activity, there appeared very great changes in the protein content of the cytoplasm of the corresponding nerve cells. The amounts of protein in the individual cell could be brought down to less than one-third of the normal content. That means that the major part of the cellular protein disappeared and must later be restored by the very same protein-forming system described above (Figure 47). Figure 66 shows cells from resting guinea pigs and from animals in a state of motor exhaustion, and the accompanying curves show from the analysis a very great difference in the total content of proteins. During the period of rest the protein content in the cytoplasm is brought up to the normal level again. During the sensory stimulation (Figure 67), the material analyzed showed almost immediately indications that the protein-forming system was being stimulated to intense activity. During the course of the very strong stimulation, the system was, however, overwhelmed by the demand upon it, and the protein content decreased rapidly (1945, 3). In recent years extensive work has been performed by Hamberger and Hydén in order to find out whether these changes occur under the *normal* function of the nerve cell. Working on the VIIIth brain nerve they found, in different ways, that changes of the character described are quite conspicuous within the ordinary ranges of irritation. Especially interesting were their findings of simultaneous changes in higher centers, which prove a transneuronal activity—which might be a promising lead for further work on localization in the nervous system. The present evidence leads to the conclusion that conspicuous changes

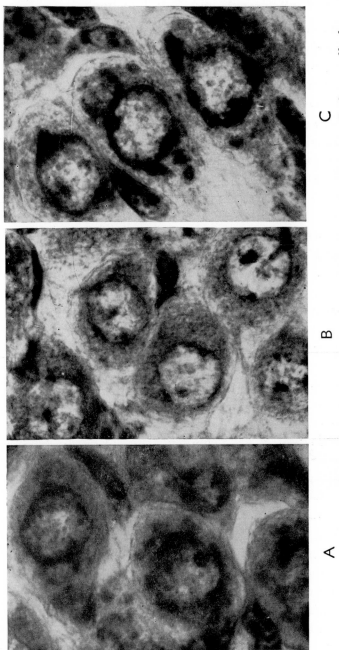

A

B

C

Figure 67. A, Cells from cochlear ganglion of rabbit representing the average appearance. B, Same cell after heavy acoustic stimulation, signs of regeneration are appearing. C, Regeneration after heavy acoustic stimulation, evident from collections of nucleotides in cytoplasm around the nuclear membrane and increase in protein.

in protein metabolism of the adult nerve cells are correlated with the nerve function. These results gave even more than was hoped for, as they removed the one apparent exception from general applicability of the diagram in Figure 47 (cf. above).

The peculiar organization of the protein-forming system in the nerve cell has thus been simply explained by the fact that correlated with its function we find very profound changes in the state of its proteins, and that during intense activity its protein-forming system, according to Figure 47, must be able to replace used protein rapidly. The nerve cell organization is thus determined by the necessity of its being ready to produce protein with great speed on any occasion.

When the total mass of the cell body increases during *regenerative* processes, this system works as in other cells. Extensive studies on regenerating nerve cells (Hydén, 1943, 5) showed that in regeneration after sectioning the axon, the events which are illustrated by Figure 68 occur (1943, 5, p. 109). The pictures in Figure 69 illustrate the stages marked a, b, e and f in Figure 68. The general course is as follows: On excision of the axon the normal function stops. During the first days after the excision, the content of nucleotides and proteins diminishes considerably, the protein-forming system showing every sign of intense irritation. After about two

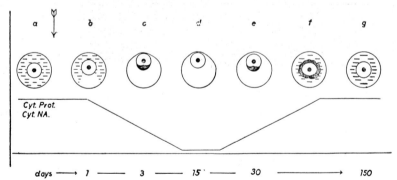

FIGURE 68. Diagram of changes in the protein-forming processes after excision of the axon. The ordinate indicates the amounts of nucleotides and proteins in the ganglion cell cytoplasm. The numbers show the lapse of time after excision of the axon (marked by arrow).

weeks the amount of nucleotides and cytoplasmic proteins is very low in the cell, and after another short period signs of returning cell activity are apparent in the shape of some increase of nucleolar substances, in the appearance of large amounts of cytoplasmic

a   b

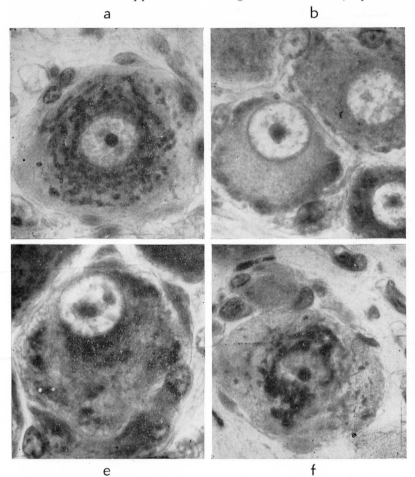

e   f

FIGURE 69. Cells corresponding to the stages a, b, e, f in the diagram in Figure 68.

nucleotides around the nuclear membrane, and in a parallel increase in the cytoplasmic masses of the cell as a whole. The series of changes demonstrates very nicely how the system for cytoplasmic protein formation starts to work again after having been hurt, starting as shown in Figure 47.

With the correlation between nucleoprotein metabolism and nerve cell function in mind, Hydén and Hartelius tried to affect the function of the nerve cell by stimulating the nucleoprotein formation in the cell by chemical means. Malononitrile and some other organic nitriles are known to cause chromatolytic changes in nerve cells. Hydén shows that these changes in this case corresponded to what was cytochemically interpreted as a stimulation of the cytoplasmic protein-forming system of the nerve cell (1948, 3). Treating rabbits with the substance mentioned, they noticed a stimulation, judged cytochemically, in different parts of the nervous system and also a neurological phenomenon indicating functional stimulation (Figure 70). In animals, however, it is very difficult to judge such general stimulation of the nervous system. These observations by Hydén and Hartelius have led them to experiments to treat certain mental conditions in man by malononitriles. The basis for this was the probability that in some mental disorders the system of cytoplasmic protein formation in groups of nerve cells was disturbed, a proposition which is supported by as yet very limited observations of pathological cases. The first clinical results attained in certain mental conditions showed, in general, a marked stimulation of psychic function in the cases investigated. For details the reader is referred to the original paper. An interesting beginning seems to have been made here for further work. For the fundamental studies, which are the topic of this presentation, these experiments are of interest since they indicate clearly that not only motor and sensory nerve cell function, but also that connected with psychic activities is influenced by the endocellular system for cytoplasmic protein formation described above.

3. ORGANIZATION DURING DIFFERENTIATION

We have seen examples showing how the cytoplasmic protein-forming system operates during growth and during the functional activity of some adult tissues. For the cells of higher organisms there is, between the period of growth and maturity, a time of differentiation in which the cell undergoes a special development to suit its task in the organism.

Large complexes of genes operate in the system for cytoplasmic protein formation, resulting in the production of primary gene products in such large amounts that, among other things, they seem to form the major part of the large nucleolar masses in these stages. When growth ceases and differentiation starts, quantitatively very inclusive chemical functions of other gene complexes also are to be expected. Since these genes might possibly be expected to work by a similar nucleolar mechanism, we may have the opportunity to make a cytochemical study of gene function and nuclear organization during early differentiation.

There is another aspect of the differentiation process that makes it of special interest to us here, namely, the opportunity to study cytochemically certain pathological disturbances in mammalian tissues. It is a well-known fact that a number of such pathological states start with conspicuous disturbances in the differentiation process.

Thorell has been occupied with cytochemical analyses of some of these problems of which a few examples will be given (1944, 2, 4; 1945, 2, 4, 6; 1946, 2; 1947, 17, 18, 19; 1948, 4, 5, 6). Most comprehensive is the study of hematopoiesis. The intensity of the growth of the individual cell can be judged from the organization of its system for cytoplasmic protein formation. Thorell has developed a technique to determine the hemoglobin content of individual red blood corpuscles during the course of their development. This content is used as a measure of the degree of differentiation of the cell. Figure 71 (upper row) shows some complete absorption spectra in ultraviolet and visible regions for areas in the cytoplasm of red blood cells in different stages of development. It was found that during normal development differentiation first starts at a stage when growth is practically finished. In a series of different pathological conditions, the relations between differentiation and growth were found to be changed in a way which was sometimes characteristic for certain pathological conditions. The lower row in Figure 71 shows how in pernicious anemia the ratio between the speed of differentiation and the development of the system for cytoplasmic growth is radically changed. Thorell has also

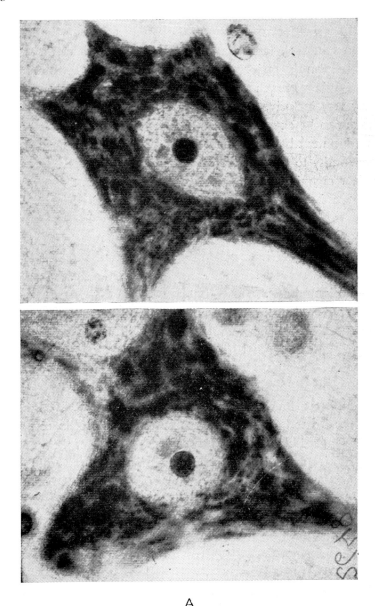

A

FIGURE 70. Anterior horn cell from rabbits photographed under as identical conditions as possible (Hydén and Hartelius). A, Untreated animal.

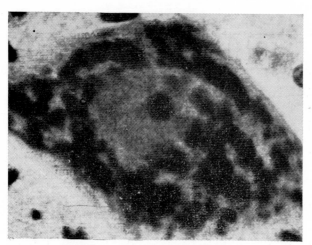

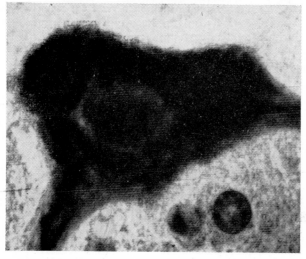

B

B, Rabbit treated with 4 mg. malonodinitrile per kg. body weight and killed after one hour.

studied the development of the dentine cells in the guinea pig tooth. The course of the differentiation in this case has been followed by measuring the amount of calcium and phosphate in the individual cells with the aid of Engström's X-ray microspectrophotometric procedures. Here, also, the processes of differentiation started after growth had ceased. The reversibility of differentiation

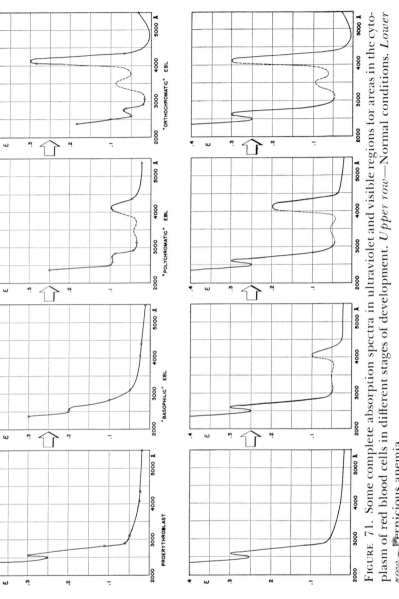

FIGURE 71. Some complete absorption spectra in ultraviolet and visible regions for areas in the cytoplasm of red blood cells in different stages of development. *Upper row*—Normal conditions. *Lower row*—Pernicious anemia.

nd that

ividual

ciency,

lasmic

inter-

OWTH

abolic

ese re-

rotein

tically

TIN

N

hly

(1)
sis of
cytopl

(2)
with
an ide
thus a

(3)
ductic
in diff
tion.
units
worth
ably

(4)
strict
time
prod
ing
ribos

CHAPTER VI

Disturbed systems for protein formation in the metazoan cell

THE SUMMARY at the end of the last chapter shows that the organization of the metazoan nucleus, with regard to the systems for protein formation, can be referred back to simple premises. The next problem is the study of the detailed organization of the nucleus itself in the metazoan cell.

Aims in that direction have several times been referred to above. Here should briefly be mentioned, however, two approaches aiming at the same fundamental problem—the organization of the normal cell—but using the peculiar properties of certain specialized cells. The approaches referred to are:

(1) Studies of cells in which the system of protein formation has been changed.

(2) Analyses of organisms (such as bacteria and viruses) in which the organelles for the protein formation system are less complete than that of higher organisms and must be assumed to be organized in a more primitive way. The latter case will be treated in Chapter VII.

The most conspicuous of all metazoan cells with changed growth mechanism are tumor cells. Another striking example is a virus-infected cell, because of the fact that the virus acts as a parasite on the very organelles of the system in which we are interested. This will be treated in Chapter VII. Studies are being carried out on experimentally induced modifications of the function of the systems in question (e.g., by chemical means).

Microspectrographic studies of tumors have been carried through on about 50 different cases of human carcinomas by Santesson and the author (1941, 3; 1942, 2; 1943, 4; 1944, 1; 1948, 8). The results were very uniform for all the different types investigated. Different parts of the same carcinoma show great differences in the functional development of the system for cytoplasmic protein formation. Figure 73 shows two pictures from a section of a very malignant mammary tumor. The ultraviolet photographs show at once very pronounced differences in the amount of cytoplasmic nucleotides in different regions of the tumor. Closer study of the development of the different organelles of the system for protein formation in the cytoplasm shows that throughout the whole of the tumor this system was very markedly stimulated. However, the corresponding excessive functional activity is found only in a restricted number of cells. Thus, all tumor cells could be classified between two well-defined extreme types, illustrated in Figure 75. One type, which we shall call A, is characterized by extreme stimulation and extreme activity of the system for protein formation. The other type, which we shall call B, is characterized by an extreme stimulation but little or no activity of the same system. In the B cell the nucleolar apparatus shows signs of intense function, but practically no protein or nucleic-acid formation occurs in the cytoplasm. These conditions are further illustrated by the series of absorption spectra arranged in Figure 74.

The A cells are found especially in the regions where the nutritional conditions are good, as, for instance, in the outer part of cancer rods and in the neighborhood of blood vessels. The actively invading cells are also of this type.

A thorough study of the different tumors shows that the observations just cited can be applied quite generally and that they may be condensed into the diagram shown in Figure 75 (1942, 2, p. 77). The different curves show what happens during the transition from

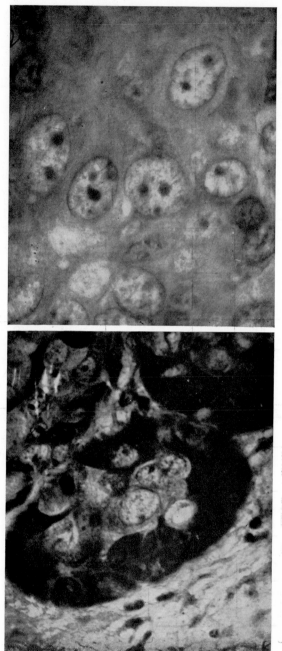

FIGURE 73. Two parts of same cancer rod in a mammary carcinoma. *Left*—Area with A cells. *Right*—Area with B cells.

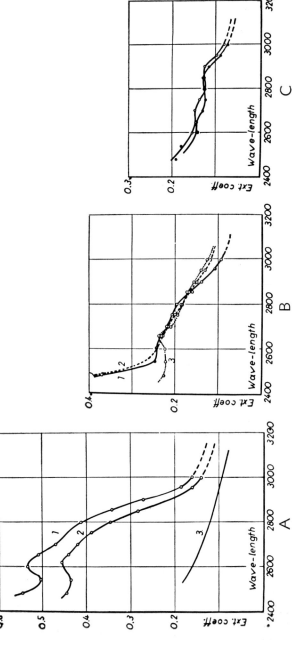

FIGURE 74. Absorption spectra of points in cytoplasm of cells of A-type, B-type, and cells in incipient necrosis.

A to B. In the A cell all the different organelles of the cytoplasmic protein-forming system are very well developed, and the cell shows all indications of excessive protein formation. In the B cell the nucleus still shows the organization typical for a cell in rapid protein production, but no further increase of protein or ribose nucleotides occurs in the cytoplasm. All the cancer cells in a given preparation may be placed in this diagram as intermediate stages between what may be called the extreme A-type on the one side, through the extreme B-type, passing over to a necrotic type on the other side.

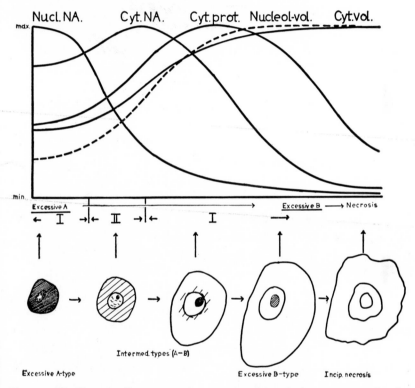

FIGURE 75. Rough diagrammatic presentation of the processes in the development from A cell to B cell. The curves represent only the *general course* and their points do not indicate exact figures.

Nucl. NA = nuclear nucleic acid. Cyt. NA = quantity (not concentration) of cytoplasmic nucleic acid. Nucleol. vol. = nucleolar volume. Cyt. vol. = cytoplasmic volume. I = area where the development of the system of protein formation is such that the cell can be distinguished from normal cells. II = area where the cell cannot be distinguished from normal cells in active growth.

The fact that all cells can be arranged according to the organization of their system for protein formation in such a diagram must indicate that a real development from the one type to the other occurs. Other factors, for instance the general arrangement in the tumor cords, point in the same direction. In the outer zones, richest in A cells, one finds rapid growth and division, during the course of which some of the cells lying at the surface become entirely surrounded by other cells and sink towards the center of the cord. Parallel with this, the sunken cells change towards the excessive B-type, cease to grow, rarely divide, and show all transitional stages towards necrosis.

Figure 76 shows another example of the same phenomenon but in a bladder carcinoma. The A, B, and intermediary cells from the carcinoma show clearly different degrees of functional activity in the system for cytoplasmic protein formation. In Figure 77 the absorption spectra of points in the cytoplasms of cells of corresponding stages are plotted.

These observations permit us to interpret the variegated picture of a cancerous tumor by arranging the cells in different stages along a developmental chain. The question then arises whether or not all these cells have some common characteristics that distinguish them from normal cells. The development of the protein-forming system in A-type as well as B-type cells differs markedly from that in the normal cell even when the latter is in a state of rapid growth. Between the malignant tumor cell and the normally growing cell there seems to exist a fundamental difference in regard to the development of the system for protein formation. In the malignant tumor cell the endocellular inhibitory mechanism, which normally limits the activity of the protein-forming system, has more or less ceased to function, leading to specific alterations in the cytochemical picture. As the nucleolus-associated chromatin (or heterochromatin) is a leading factor in the system for cytoplasmic protein formation, it is evident that it and the genes which regulate its function must play a prominent rôle not only in the growth of the cancer cell but also in carcinogenesis.

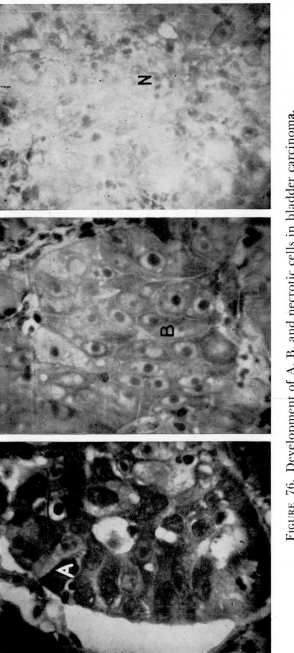

FIGURE 76. Development of A, B, and necrotic cells in bladder carcinoma.

This deduction makes analysis of the changes in the cell during carcinogenesis of importance for the study of the regulation of the protein metabolism of the normal cell. Figure 78 (left photograph) demonstrates a regenerating skin, that is, a normal skin in which fairly rapid growth processes are occurring. The right-hand photograph is of a very early skin carcinoma. It is evident that the cyto-

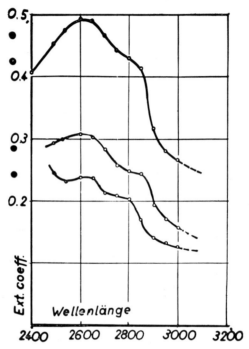

FIGURE 77. Absorption spectra of points in the cytoplasms of cells of corresponding stages in Figure 76.

plasmic nucleotides and also the size of the nucleoli have increased enormously. An especially instructive example has been studied by Moberger (1945, 9). In giant follicular hyperplasia of lymph nodes, often called Symer's disease, there is a change from a condition best described as hyperplasia to a real reticular cell sarcoma. The ultra-violet analysis demonstrates a continuous change in the activity of the system for protein formation. Figure 79 is taken from Stowell's work on liver (1948, 10). The left-hand picture shows a normal

indicates that they are of ribose type, and solubility studies show that most of them are polynucleotides. When the culture gets old and growth ceases, the cell picture changes back to the one first illustrated. The increase in ribose polynucleotide occurs only during growth processes. If the yeast carries out an intense metabolic proc-

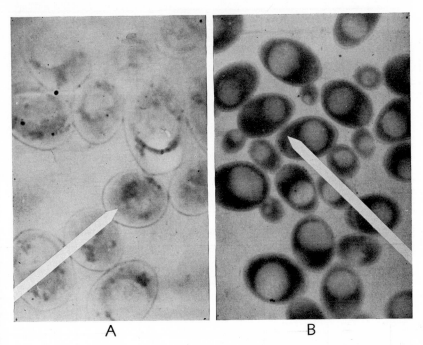

A   B

FIGURE 80. A, Yeast cells in an old, not-growing culture. Note ribose nucleotide containing granules in each cell. B, Same culture transferred to suitable medium and rapidly growing. The photographs are taken under identical conditions.

ess not accompanied by growth, for instance fermentation in the absence of a nitrogen source, the nucleotides do not increase.

Discussion.—As in the cases described above, just as we have seen in all the other cells we have considered so far, yeast cells show large changes in ribose polynucleotide content simultaneously with the increase of cell-body proteins. These nucleotides appear first immediately around the highly absorbing granules referred to above. This is especially evident when cells are grown at low tem-

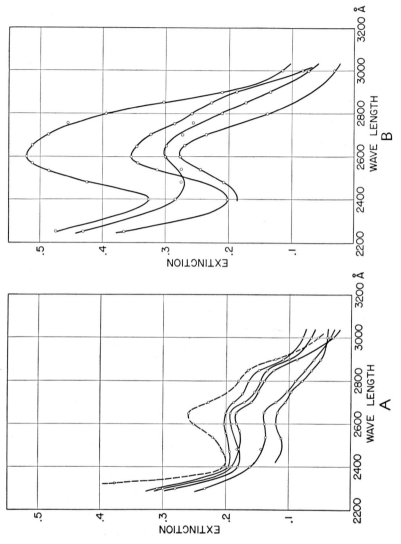

FIGURE 81. Absorption curves of points in cytoplasms of yeast cell. A and B cells as in Figure 80 A and B, respectively.

perature to slow down the rate of growth. There is a good analogy
with the nuclear membrane of more highly organized cells, where
the ribose nucleotides appear first at the nuclear membrane. A
working hypothesis is that these granules fulfill a function which in
more highly organized cells belongs to the nucleolus-associated
chromatin or heterochromatin. There is, however, one great difference: they do not contain any ribodesose nucleic acid. But then
they never enter into a chromosome structure. Observations by
previous authors have shown the presence of small ribodesose
nucleotide-containing chromosomes. Thus, the yeast cell has an
organization which seems to be analogous to that of the metazoan
nucleus with regard to its system for protein formation: It consists
of gene-carrying chromosomes characterized by ribodesose nucleic
acid, an equivalent to euchromatin in addition to a group of separate organelles, equivalents to the nucleolus-associated chromatin or
heterochromatin. Thus there seem to be at least two kinds of dis-
tinguishable structures which must co-operate to do the job of the
metazoan nucleus. The latter appears to represent a higher developmental stage in which a primary cell organelle for cytoplasmic protein production, an heterochromatin equivalent, has been taken up
by the chromosome in order to ensure its exact redistribution to the
daughter cells (*see* Figure 82).

Attention is drawn to the fact that the mechanism described here
derives from studies which specialized on the protein metabolism
of the cell. It does not exclude the possibility in higher organisms
of still more cellular structures performing specialized tasks, generally referred to the cell nucleus. For that reason work is being
done also on other groups of lower organisms, primarily protozoa.

A. ON THE NEWLY FORMED CELL-BODY PROTEINS

Here reference should be made to a theoretical difficulty which
seemed at one time insurmountable. In yeast we observe an enormous increase in cell-body protein in the presence of nucleotides
which seem to arise from a group of organelles containing ribose
nucleotides. In the metazoan cell described above the same thing

occurs at the nuclear membrane, governed by the nucleolus system and the nucleolus-associated chromatin of which the latter probably correspond to what is commonly described as heterochromatin.

As pointed out above, every structure, where we can trace a linear arrangement of the gene material and the ensuing equal partition

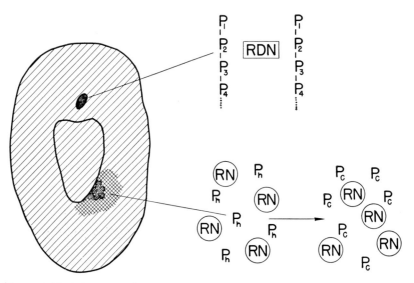

FIGURE 82. Diagram of system for protein formation in yeast-type cells.

of hereditary matter between the daughter cells, is characterized by nucleic acids of the ribodesose type (possibly plus some ribose acids). On the other hand, the organelles described as concerned with cell-body protein production in yeast are distributed at random at divisions and contain a ribose polynucleotide which has not such a *stable*, high polymeric molecular arrangement as the ribodesose polynucleotide. Furthermore, we meet these ribose nucleotides on the nuclear membrane in cells of higher organisms in cytoplasmic protein synthesis. Another thing of interest is that the observations on the cytological structure of heterochromatin in general indicate that it does not possess a linear structure nearly to such an extent as the euchromatin. To this might be added that observations of accessory chromosomes in various materials may be interpreted in the way that different closely related organisms and even cells in the same organism can contain different amounts of heterochromatin. The observations above indicate, furthermore, that in the metabolically very active cells the chromatic materials are less dense than in the less active cells. This is so consistent in large series of different cell material that it seems justified to use this as an indication pointing to metabolic work of the genes in question. According to that view, one would expect that the gene groups connected with cytoplasmic protein synthesis would to a larger extent be spread in the nucleus in cells in intense cytoplasmic formation, that is, a large part of them would be at work. This can, in fact, be traced and many examples can be cited. One of the best is the common occurrence of large, dense, heterochromatic masses in spermatocytes, for instance of insects, while in the corresponding stages of oocyte development with enormous protein formation these cannot often be traced. In the cases investigated, for example Tipula (Bauer and Caspersson) where chromatic masses can be observed in the oocyte, the cytochemical study shows a very great metabolic activity, evident from the large masses of nucleolar substances appearing inside these irregular "caryospheres" which thus cannot directly be compared with the well-defined heterochromatic chromosome parts of the spermatocyte. In this connection reference should also be made to the remarkable fact that a number of the different mechanisms of "Keimbahn-Bestimmung" (1941, 2), for instance the classical Ascaris case, all work out in the direction of transferring the largest possible quantity of heterochromatin to the egg cell or its nurse cells—the cells with the most comprehensive protein formation in the body. In the other cells of the body these large quantities would not be necessary and would remain partially inactive.

The group of apparently loosely connected facts presented in the last paragraph gives us a picture of the nucleolus-associated chromatin, and a corresponding picture of the heterochromatin, as consisting of a large group of genes differing from the euchromatic genes in that they are not equally distributed at division in some organisms, that they are not necessarily linked in a very strict linear arrangement which would result in exact distribution at division, and, furthermore, that their total amount may differ in different tissues.

As working hypothesis for the time being, which must be carefully separated from the experimental data presented in the other parts of this book, the most probable explanation seems to be that, compared with euchromatin, there are a large number of genes of a limited number of kinds of that character in the heterochromatin system. That leads, however, to the difficult conclusion that it is only reasonable to assume that in these often extremely rapid growth processes in the cytoplasm, proteins of a comparatively limited number of different kinds could reasonably be manufactured. This does not suit the general assumption of the main part of the proteins acting as enzyme carriers of a variety of different kinds in interphase. Now this difficult theoretical conclusion seems to be, in principle, overcome by the findings of the process of enzyme adaptation which could explain a change of material from one enzyme carrier to another as well as from a "basic protein of the cell" to enzyme carriers.

It should be noted that further discussion on this subject can only be carried along on the basis of vastly expanded material, primarily concerning the general organization of the nucleus throughout the whole of the developmental chain, and especially the analysis of the presently very complex conception "heterochromatin." This working hypothesis is cited here only to serve as an indication of the way in which the observations referred to in this book can be brought in connection with certain other lines of chemical approach.

2. BACTERIA

Induced by the promising results on yeast several investigators, especially Berndt Malmgren, have carried through extensive investigations on bacteria.

The first experiments (Figure 83) showed that the very great

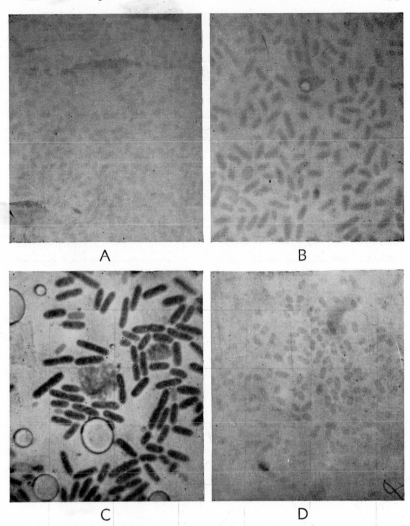

FIGURE 83. Photographs of living bacteria, taken under identical photographic conditions at different stages of growth. A, Before the transfer to suitable medium. B, Beginning of lag phase. C, Period of most rapid growth. D, End of growth.

changes looked for in the nucleic-acid content of single bacteria occur during the course of growth (1945, 5; 1947, 9–16). Figure 84 shows, among other things, a growth curve of a bacterial culture (*E.coli*) in common broth. The absorption of living cells at the wave length of the maximum absorption of the nucleic acids is very high at the end of the lag phase.

In order to search for a quantitative correlation between the bacterial growth and nucleic-acid metabolism, it was necessary for different reasons to try to make determinations of the amount of nucleic acids within one single bacterium. That has proved to be technically one of the most difficult tasks we have undertaken. The method used was, in principle, the following simple one: Absorption spectra obtained on single bacteria show that within a comparatively narrow limit of error the extinction at 2600 Å. could be used as a measure of its total nucleic-acid content, and, furthermore, that the most important sources of error are of such a nature that they are largely eliminated when comparisons are made on the same culture in different stages of growth. The results for a strain of bacteria are presented in Figure 84. The extinction at 2570 Å. of

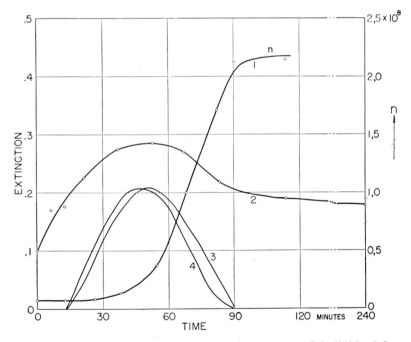

FIGURE 84. Relations between nucleotide content of individual bacterium and speed of synthesis of bacterial protein.

about two hundred cells was measured photographically at each of the times indicated after inoculation. The curves represent the quantitative evaluation of the changes shown in the previous figure. Curve 1 gives the number of bacteria, curve 2 the average extinction at 2570 Å. of individual bacteria, and curve 4 the extinction curve after subtraction of the threshold value at initiation of division. In the lag phase, before the actual division has started, nucleotide synthesis begins. When the nucleotide content has reached a certain level, it starts to fall until, when division ceases, it has reached approximately the same threshold value as when the division started. The average rate at which an individual bacterium divides may be expressed as $dn/n.dt$, where n is the number of bacteria (which in this case runs parallel with the amount of bacterial proteins) and t is time. If this function is multiplied by an arbitrary factor and plotted as in curve 3, it will be found that within the limits of error its general course corresponds well with the nucleotide curve shown here also.

Measurements, carried through by the investigators mentioned above, on a number of different bacteria have all agreed in showing that the time at which the nucleotide content is maximum closely coincides with the time at which most rapid formation of new bacterial protein takes place (1947, 9–16). This correspondence indicates that the rate of the protein synthesis is approximately proportional to the nucleotide content.

It is thus possible to show on this material just as in the metazoan cell that a ribose nucleotide cycle exists in the cell body and, furthermore, that very strong indications could be obtained for a fairly simple kinetic relationship between the nucleotide content and the rate of protein synthesis. Malmgren and Hedén's recently published papers are referred to for further details (1947, 9–16).

The data show that bacteria have a ribose nucleotide mechanism for the production of cell-body proteins, similar to that described for yeast, and that the characteristics of the material make it far more easily accessible for quantitative cytochemical work. The presence of ribodesose nucleotide-containing structures, which

divide at cell division, has been demonstrated by previous investigators and has been confirmed by these studies. Thus the most
conspicuous parts of what was described above as a nuclear system
in yeast cells occur in all bacteria investigated. It is not possible at
present to go further with the cytochemical analysis of such small
objects, but already the existing data make it appear that probably
the nuclear apparatus of bacterial cells is arranged along the same
lines we have just seen in yeast.

3. VIRUSES (1945, 8; 1948, 7)

In this group we meet organisms of varying degrees of complexity, from the simplest viruses, which contain so far as we know
only one protein group, to large forms representing transitions to
the bacteria.

The chemical data available from the work of different investigators show that the unimolecular viruses studied contain ribose
nucleotides and that the larger viruses contain either ribodesose
nucleotides alone or both kinds. Only a few large viruses have as
yet been investigated chemically, but observations with the Feulgen
reaction furnish evidence on this point for a number of other forms.
In principle, this agrees well with the idea above that ribodesose
nucleotides are specially adapted for the reproduction processes of
the gene string.

A. VIRUSES CONTAINING RIBODESOSE NUCLEIC ACID DURING REPRODUCTION

Molluscum contagiosum

A good example of a highly organized virus, containing both
kinds of nucleotides during its stages of reproduction, is *Molluscum
contagiosum*. It develops in the cytoplasm of the host cells. Thanks
to the characteristic structure of the molluscum colonies, it is possible to follow the development of the virus by investigating different layers of the infected part of the skin. The photographs in
Figures 85 and 86 and the diagram in Figure 87 demonstrate the
course of the infection. In noninfected cells the nucleoli are small

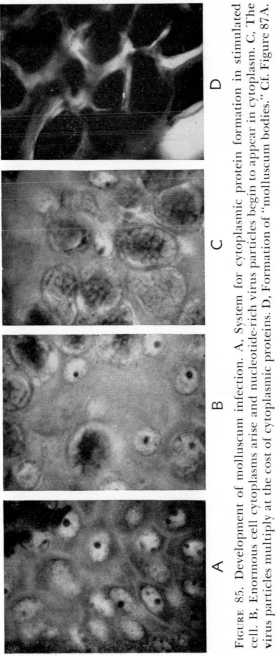

FIGURE 85. Development of molluscum infection. A, System for cytoplasmic protein formation in stimulated cell. B, Enormous cell cytoplasms arise and nucleotide-rich virus particles begin to appear in cytoplasm. C, The virus particles multiply at the cost of cytoplasmic proteins. D, Formation of "molluscum bodies." Cf. Figure 87A.

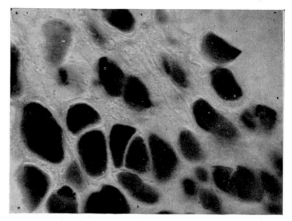

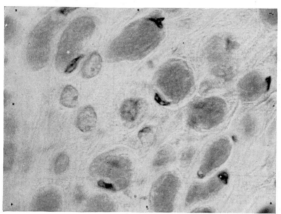

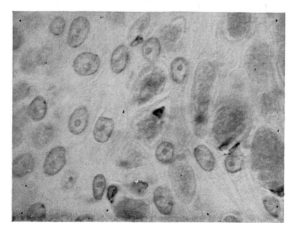

FIGURE 86. As in Figure 85 but Feulgen reaction, showing that the cytoplasmic inclusions contain ribodesose nucleotides.

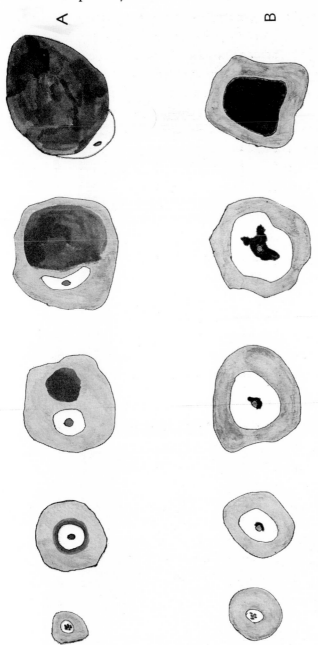

FIGURE 87. Diagrammatic presentation of development of (A) molluscum infection and (B) *Verruca vulgaris* infection.

and appear as dark spots on the photograph, mainly because of the nucleolus-associated chromatin surrounding them. The cytoplasm is poor in nucleic acids. The first sign of the infection is an enlargement of the cell cytoplasm, caused by an increase in the amount of protein. Of course, the system for protein formation is very active, for the nucleoli grow very large and ribose nucleotides collect in the cytoplasm, especially close to the nuclear membrane. After the cell has attained a certain size, a network of ultraviolet-absorbing material appears in the cytoplasm. This network finally fills the whole of the cytoplasm and contracts into dense nucleic-acid-rich bodies, the molluscum bodies, which are known to contain the virus element. The Feulgen reaction shows that the nucleic acid is of ribodesose type.

Briefly the events during the development of the infection can be interpreted as follows (Figures 85, 86, 87):

At first the infected epithelial cells are stimulated to very intense production of cytoplasmic proteins. The material resulting from this process is transformed by the virus into large bodies containing masses of protein and desoxyribose nucleotides in large concentrations. They are agglomerates of the molluscum elementary bodies.

Verruca vulgaris

The course of the infection is very similar to that of *Molluscum contagiosum*. This virus, however, develops *inside* the nucleus. Different stages in the development of the infections are shown in Figure 87 and the series of photographs in Figure 88. The first changes observed are the same nuclear alterations that we saw in the molluscum infection, namely signs of intense stimulation of the nucleolar apparatus. It is a striking feature, however, that the increase in cytoplasmic protein does not correspond to the extent of changes in the nucleus. As the nucleolus grows, heavily absorbing substances appear in the nucleus around it. At first they resemble the nucleolus-associated chromatin, but soon they increase at a rapid rate and ultimately fill the greater part of the nucleus. Finally they join together to form aggregates similar to the molluscum

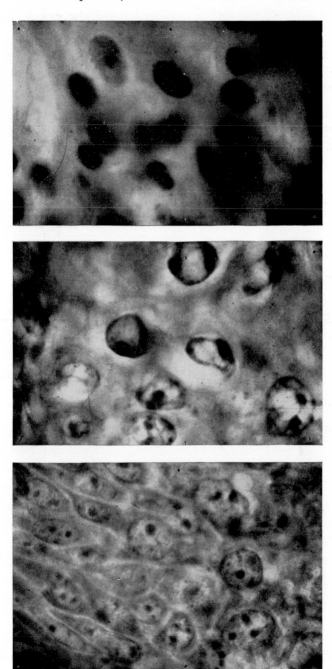

FIGURE 88. Development of verruca infection in ultraviolet photographs.

bodies, while the remainder of the cell dies. The cytochemical changes which occur in both these types of infected cell may be summarized in the following way: Large quantities of a foreign substance containing desoxyribose nucleotide appear in the cell. These substances coalesce to form large structures, corresponding to the large cell inclusions found by previous investigators. We assume that these masses represent the virus masses. In the case of molluscum, they are localized in the cytoplasm, in that of verruca, in the nucleus.

In both cases, the host cells are initially stimulated to intensive protein production, but the product of this process is consumed by

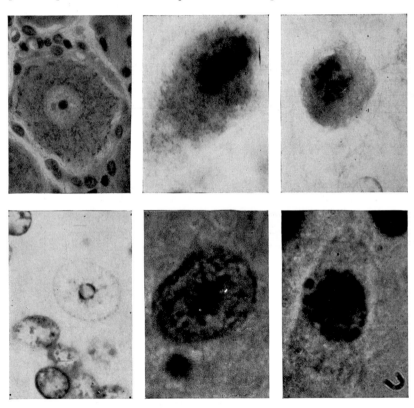

FIGURE 89. Rabies infection of nerve cell, different stages from left to right showing appearance. *Above*—Ultraviolet photographs. *Below*—Feulgen pictures.

the viruses themselves, which reproduce with the aid of nucleotides. Thus the viruses exploit the nucleoprotein-forming organelles of the host cells in order to fulfill their own needs for reproduction. In the first case, the virus acts as a parasite on the cytoplasmic part of the normal protein-forming apparatus, while in the second case it attacks at the nucleolar level.

Rabies

This infection, studied in the early stages, shows a development closely resembling that of the skin virus verruca (Figure 89).

B. VIRUSES NOT CONTAINING RIBODESOSE NUCLEOTIDES

Poliomyelitis

In general, it can be said that the nerve cells, thanks to their size, form an excellent material for the study of virus reproduction. Figure 90 demonstrates an infection with a virus, poliomyelitis, where ribose-nucleotide-rich new masses are formed in the host cell. Admittedly this is no definite proof that the virus is ribodesose-free. The pictures are from human material which was collected from cases that ended fatally after *a few days'* sickness. When working with cytochemical procedures, one also finds corresponding stages in infection of longer duration. Comprehensive work is going on on the problem of finding means of identifying virus bodies in the cell, other than the ultraviolet procedure.

The first changes which can be observed involve the nucleolar apparatus and correspond to an intense stimulation thereof, fairly similar to the stimulation by the molluscum and verruca infections. The spectrophotometric studies show a great increase in the content of proteins and ribose nucleotides of the nucleolus itself. The nucleoli can reach quite enormous dimensions. Scattered in this mass of material are small particles with a composition corresponding to that of the nucleolus-associated chromatin. The cytochemical interpretation of these pictures is that the system for the production of cytoplasmic proteins has been very intensely stimulated. At first there are corresponding changes in the cytoplasm and large amounts of ribose nucleotides may appear at the nuclear membrane. Soon, however, the cytoplasmic protein production ceases and the amount of nucleotides in the cytoplasm diminishes rapidly. The nucleolar apparatus then begins to show a corresponding sign of severe damage: its content of nucleotides and of protein decreases. As the infection progresses the nucleolar apparatus is damaged still more and the reproduction of cytoplasmic protein ceases almost entirely. In this stage the nucleus might appear filled with substances which are distinctly pathological. They appear in the ultraviolet as small granules with a fairly high absorption.

Louping ill

The virus contains ribose nucleotide and the changes correspond closely in principle to those just described for poliomyelitis. Cytochemical analysis shows that the virus attacks the very first part of the system for cytoplasmic protein formation, the nucleolus itself, and probably the nucleolus-associated chromatin. At first one sees the usual intense stimulation of the system which is followed by a transient phase of increase in the cytoplasmic proteins. In and around the nucleolus foreign ribose-nucleotide-containing masses appear.

4. DISCUSSION

If we compare the phenomena in the host cell during the reproduction of the different virus types presented above, two things are of special interest. The first is that during the time for reproduction of the viruses they contain large amounts of nucleotides. The other is that they all appear as parasites on the normal system for protein production of the host cell. In all virus infections studied by us (thus far eight kinds, 1948, 7), the first sign of the infection has been a stimulation of the cytoplasmic-forming system of the host cell. Then virus particles appear in rapidly increasing quantities at places in the cell which are different for different viruses. The simplest virus types appear close to the nucleolus-associated chromatin and the nucleolus and the higher types either there, or at the nuclear

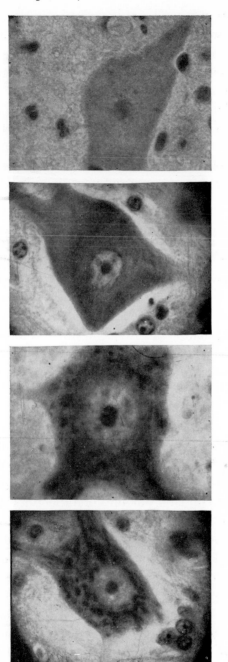

FIGURE 90. Development of poliomyelitis infection. *Left*—Normal nerve cell, then different stages of infection, involving enormous increase in nucleolar apparatus and appearance of nucleotide-containing masses in nucleus and cytoplasm.

membrane, or the cytoplasm. Thus, in general, the viruses seem to stimulate the formation of cell proteins but switch themselves in on certain stages of the synthetic processes, in that way "tapping" the chemical processes and using the substances produced for their own synthesis of virus protein. It is then natural that the simplest viruses are to be found closest to the primary organelles of the system for cytoplasmic protein formation.

The results of the study of the protein metabolic system of the normal metazoan cell have been summarized above. The organization of the organelles for protein production, which we have just described for simpler organisms, shows that the same basic outlines are found here, too. Ribose nucleotides take part in the reproduction of even the simplest viruses consisting of only one protein group. The higher types of viruses, which we must assume contain several different kinds of protein that are simultaneously multiplied and distributed to the daughter particles, have a primitive mechanism that performs at least some of the functions of the chromosomes in higher forms. They contain the otherwise chromosome-specific nucleotide, ribodesose nucleic acid (Figure 91).

The bacteria and yeast cells described have a more complex organization that includes a cell body as well as a set of genes, in a strict sense. It seems justifiable to assume that the cytoplasmic substance contains fewer kinds of protein than would be required for (or produced by) the great variety of genes found in the gene complex. We find, moreover, that the chromosome-like organelles contain ribodesose nucleotides while the small group of structures involved in the production of cell-body protein have chiefly the ribose type. When a yeast cell divides these organelles are distributed to both daughter cells, but with much less accuracy than the chromosome sets in the higher organisms (Figure 93).

The nuclei of the higher forms are organized according to the same outline but with the difference that the organelles involved in the reproduction of cytoplasmic protein are taken up by the chromosome apparatus, apparently in order to insure proper redistribution of them at cell division (Figure 92).

VIRUS REPRODUCTION

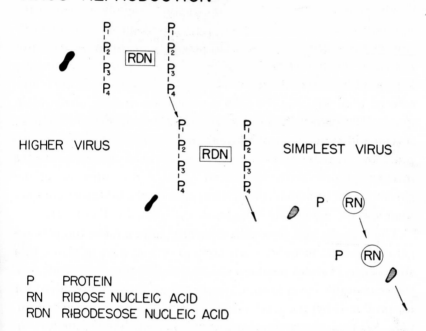

P   PROTEIN
RN   RIBOSE NUCLEIC ACID
RDN RIBODESOSE NUCLEIC ACID

FIGURE 91. Protein metabolism of two classes of viruses.

CHAPTER VIII

General survey

THE AIM OF the studies presented in this book in a summarizing way has been the analysis, by aid of specially developed quantitative cytochemical procedures, of endocellular processes accompanying growth and function of cells. Interest has primarily been centered on the rôle of various cell organelles in the processes leading to protein synthesis.

It has been shown that the systems for protein formation in nucleus and cytoplasm in the metazoan cell work according to uniform lines of general applicability throughout the animal kingdom.

Short surveys have been given above of the technique and the results: Technique, Chapter II, paragraph 6 and Chapter III, paragraph 3; Protein metabolism of the nucleus and the mitotic cycle, Chapter IV, paragraph 7; Protein metabolism of the cytoplasm, Chapter V, paragraph 4; General organization of the nucleus, Chapter VII, paragraph 4.

Figures 92, 93, and 94 give a short summarizing presentation of some more important points of general validity. Among these points the following general ones should be mentioned: The polynucleotides participate in the processes for cellular protein synthesis of the cytoplasm as well as that of the nucleus. *In the reproduction of the linearly arranged gene-chain (chromosome), the nucleic acids are of the ribodesose type. In the production of the not-so-strictly linearly arranged proteins, as in the case of the formation of the cytoplasmic proteins and reproduction of simple viruses,* and

VIRUS REPRODUCTION

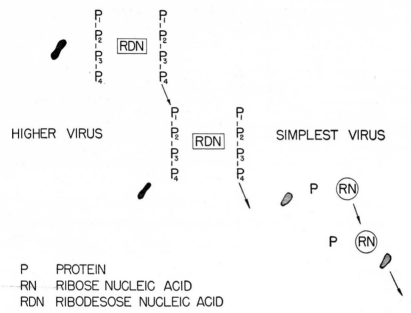

HIGHER VIRUS

SIMPLEST VIRUS

P   PROTEIN
RN   RIBOSE NUCLEIC ACID
RDN RIBODESOSE NUCLEIC ACID

FIGURE 94. Protein metabolism of two classes of viruses. *Above*—Higher types of viruses, carrying several gene-protein groups and thus a primitive chromosome mechanism to ensure proper redistribution, have ribodesose nucleic acids at reproduction (eventually, Plus ribose acids during "function"). *Below*—Viruses containing one protein group do not need the chromosome mechanism and thus contain only the ribose-type nucleic acids.

Bibliography

1932, 1 Caspersson, T., "Die quantitative Bestimmung vom Thymonucleinsäure mittels fuchsinschwefliger Säure." *Biochem. Z.* 253:97.

1932, 2 Caspersson, T., "Zur Kenntnis der Optik weisser Sole. I. Theoretische Ableitung des Absorptionskoeffizienten." *Kolloid-Z.* 60:151.

1933, 1 Caspersson, T., "Zur Kenntnis der Optik weisser Sole. II. Die diffuse Seitenstrahlung." *Kolloid-Z.* 65:162.

1933, 2 Caspersson, T., "Zur Kenntnis der Optik weisser Sole. III. Die optischen Verhältnisse bei der Koagulation." *Kolloid-Z.* 65:301.

1934, 1 Caspersson, T., "Ultraviolettmikroskopien och dess användningsområden." *Nord. Med.* 7:337.

1934, 2 Caspersson, T. and Holmgren, Hj. "Variationen der Kerngrösse während der verschiedenen Phasen der Leberarbeit." *Anat. Anz.* 79:53.

1934, 3 Caspersson, T., "Druckfiltrierung von Thymonucleinsäure." *Biochem. Z.* 270:161.

1935, 1 Caspersson, T., Hammarsten, E., and Hammarsten, H., "Interactions of proteins and nucleic acid." *Transact. Faraday Soc.* 31:367.

1935, 2 Caspersson, T., "Chromosomstrukturen in lebenden Zellen." *Naturwissenschaften* 23:500.

1936, 1 Caspersson, T., "Uber den chemischen Aufbau der strukturen des Zellkernes." *Skand. Arch. Physiol.* 73, Suppl. nr. 8.

1936, 2 Caspersson, T., "Die Absorptionsmessung im mikroskopischen Präparat als mikrochemische Methode." *Skand. Arch. Physiol.* 77.

1936, 3 Caspersson, T., "Die Untersuchung der Nukleinsäureverteilung im Zellkern." *Z. wiss. Mikr. u. mikr. Technik.* 53:403.

1937, 1 Caspersson, T., "Exposé sur la répartition des acides nucléques dans le noyau cellulaire." *Bull. Histol. Appl.* 14:33.

1937, 2 Caspersson, T., Über den chemischen Aufbau der Strukturen des Zellkernes." *Protoplasma.* 27:463.

1937, 3 Caspersson, T., Über die Verteilung der Nukleinsäure in dem Zellkern." *Arch. exp. Zellforsch. Gewebezüch* 19:217.

1937, 4 Caspersson, T., "Methoden zur physikalischen Analyse der Zellstruktur." *Fortschr. Zool.* 2:270.

1937, 5 Caspersson, T., "Die Wirkungen der verschiedenen Arten von Strahlung auf die Zelle." *Fortschr. Zool.* 2:288.

1938, 1 Caspersson, T. and Hammarsten, E., "Molecular shape and size of thymonucleic acid." *Nature* 141:122.

1938, 2 Caspersson, T. and Schultz, J., "Nucleic acid metabolism of the chromosomes in relation to gene reproduction." *Nature* 142:294.

1938, 3 Caspersson, T. and Schultz, J., "Studies on the physiology of the chromosomes." "Bestimmung der Lokalisation lichtabsorbierender Stoffe in einer einzelnen Zelle." *Ur Kongressber. XVI Int. Physiol. Kongresses 1938,* Zürich.

1939, 1 Caspersson, T., "Über die Rolle der Desoxyribosenukleinsäure bei der Zellteilung." *Chromosoma* 1:147.

1939, 2 Caspersson, T. and Schultz, J. "Heterochromatic regions and the nucleic acid metabolism of the chromosomes." *Arch. exp. Zellforsch. Gewebezüch* 22:650.

1939, 3 Caspersson, T., "Studies on the nucleic acid metabolism during the cell cycle." *Arch. exp. Zellforsch. Gewebezüch* 22:655.

1939, 4 Caspersson, T. and Schultz, J., "Pentose nucleotides in the cytoplasm of growing tissues." *Nature* 143:602.

1939, 5 Caspersson, T., "Über Ultraviolettmikroskopie." *Zeiss Nachr.* 3: Heft 1–5.

1939, 6 Caspersson, T., "Die Analyse der Zellstruktur mit Hilfe von Röntgen-Elektronen- und polarisations optischen Methoden." *Fortschr. Zool.* 4:338.

1939, 7 Morgan, T. H. and Schultz, J., "Investigations on the con-

1939, 7 (Cont.) stitution of the germinal material in relation to heredity." *Carnegie Inst. Wash.* Pub. 38:273.

1939, 8 Morgan, T. H. and Schultz, J., "Investigations on the constitution of the germinal material in relation to heredity." *Carnegie Inst. Wash.* Pub. 39:251.

1939, 9 Caspersson, T., "On the role of the nucleic acid in the cell." *Proc. VII Intern. Genet. Congr.* 1939, 85.

1939, 10 Schultz, J., "The function of heterochromatin." *Proc. VII Intern. Genet. Congr.* 1939, 257.

1940, 1 Caspersson, T., "Methods for the Determination of the Absorption Spectra of Cell Structures." *J. Roy. Microscop. Soc.* 60:8.

1940, 2 Caspersson, T., "Über Eiweiss-stoffe im Chromosomgerüst." *Naturwissenschaften* 28:514.

1940, 3 Caspersson, T., "Die Eiweissverteilung in den Strukturen des Zellkerns." *Chromosoma* 1:562.

1940, 4 Caspersson, T., "Nukleinsäureketten und Genvermehrung." *Chromosoma* 1:605.

1940, 5 Caspersson, T. and Gersh, I., "Total protein and organic iodine in the colloid and cells of single follicles of the thyroid gland." *Anat. Record* 78:303.

1940, 6 Caspersson, T. and Schultz, J., "Ribonucleic acids in both nucleus and cytoplasm and the function of the nucleolus." *Proc. Nat. Acad. Sci.* (U.S.) 26:507.

1940, 7 Caspersson, T., Schultz, J., and Aquilonius, L., "The genetic control of nucleolar composition." *Proc. Nat. Acad. Sci.* (U.S.) 26:515.

1941, 1 Caspersson, T., "Einiges über optische Anisotropie und Feinbau von Chromatin und Chromosomen." *Chromosoma* 2:247.

1941, 2 Caspersson, T., "Studien über den Eiweissumsatz der Zelle." *Naturwissenschaften* 29:33.

1941, 3 Caspersson, T., Nyström, Cl., and Santesson, L., "Zytoplasmatische Nukleotide in Tumorzellen." *Naturwissenschaften* 29:29.

1941, 4 Caspersson, T. and Brandt, K., "Nucleotidumsatz und Wachstum bei Presshefe." *Protoplasma* 35:507.

1941, 5 Caspersson, T., Landström, H., and Wohlfart, G., "Über den Nucleotidumsatz der Nervenzelle." *Z. mikroskop. anat. Forsch.* 49:534.

1941, 6 Caspersson, T. and Thorell, B., "Die Lokalisation der Adenylnukleotide in der quergestreiften Muskelfaser." *Naturwissenschaften* 29:363.

1941, 7 Caspersson, T., "Några nyare rön om cellkärnans funktion." *Nord. Med.* 12:3106.

1941, 8 Caspersson, T., Landström, H., and Aquilonius, L. "Cytoplasmanukleotide in eiweissproduzierende Drüsenzellen." *Chromosoma* 2:111.

1941, 9 Brandt, K., "Physiologische Chemie und Cytologie der Presshefe." *Protoplasma* 36:77.

1941, 10 Caspersson, T. and Thorell, B., "Der endozelluläre Eiweiss- und Nukleinsäurestoffwechsel in embryonalem Gewebe." *Chromosoma* 2:132.

1942, 1 Caspersson, T. and Thorell, B., "The localisation of the adenylic acids in striated muscle-fibres." *Acta Physiol. Scand.* 4:97.

1942, 2 Caspersson, T. and Santesson, L., "Studies on protein metabolism in the cells of epithelial tumours." *Acta Radiol.* Suppl. XLVI.

1942, 3 Landström-Hydén, H., "Kemiska omsättningar i den enskilda nervcellen." *Nord. Med.* 13:144.

1942, 4 Norberg, B., "On the histo- and cytochemical determination of phosphorus." *Acta Physiol. Scand.* 5, Suppl. XIV.

1943, 1 Engström, A., "Korrelation zwischen Aschengehalt und Ultraviolettabsorption bei verschiedenen Zellbestandteilen." *Chromosoma* 2:459.

1943, 2 Hydén, H., "Die Funktion des Kernkörperchens bei der Eiweissbildung in Nervenzellen." *Z. mikroskop. Anat. Forsch.* 54:96.

1943, 3 Hydén, H. and Rexed, B., "Der Wachstumsmechanismus in den Schwannschen Zellen während der Nervenregeneration." *Z. mikroskop. Anat. Forsch.* 54:352.

1943, 4 Caspersson, T. and Santesson, L., "Om cancercellens tillväxtmekanism." *Nord. Med.* 20:1683.

1943, 5 Hydén, H., "Protein metabolism in the nerve cell during growth and function." *Acta Physiol. Scand.* 6, Suppl. XVII.

1944, 1 Caspersson, T. and Santesson, L., "Studies on protein metabolism in the cells of epithelial tumours." *Acta Radiol.* 25, 113.

1944, 2   Thorell, B. and Wising, P., "Om äggvitebildningen i myelom-cellen." *Nord. Med.* 24:1842.

1944, 3   Hydén, H., "Aggviteomsättningen i nervceller i samband med funktion." *Nord. Med.* 22:904.

1944, 4   Thorell, B., "Behaviour of the nucleolar apparatus during growth and differentiation of the normal blood cells in the adult stage." *Acta Med. Scand.* 117:334.

1944, 5   Engström, A., "The localization of mineral salts in striated musclefibres." *Acta Physiol. Scand.* 8:137.

1944, 6   Engström, A. and Hámos, L. von, "Microanalysis by secondary roentgen spectrography." *Acta Radiol.* 25:325.

1944, 7   Lange, P., "Om ligninets natur och fördelning i granved." *Svensk Papperstidn.* 11:262.

1945, 1   Hydén, H., "Funktionstillståndet i nervceller vid tigrolys." *Nord. Med.* 25:90.

1945, 2   Thorell, B., "Om nukleotidomsättninv i lymfocyterna." *Nord. Med.* 28:2115.

1945, 3   Hydén, H., and Hamberger, C.-A., "Cytochemical changes in the cochlear ganglion caused by acoustic stimulation and trauma." *Acta Oto-Laryngol.* 61, Suppl. LXI.

1945, 4   Thorell, B., Bing, J., and Fagraeus, A., "Studies on nucleic acid metabolism in plasma cells." *Acta Physiol. Scand.* 10: 282.

1945, 5   Caspersson, T., Malmgren, B., Thorell, B., and Bjerke-lund, E., "Nukleotidomsättning och kärnorganisation hos bakterier." *Nord. Med.* 28:2636.

1945, 6   Thorell, B. and Wilton, Å., "The nucleotide metabolism of the dentine cells under normal conditions and in avitamino-sis C." *Acta Path. Microbiol. Scand.* 22:593.

1945, 7   Lange, P., "Ultraviolettabsorption av fast lignin." *Svensk Papperstidn.* 48:241.

1945, 8   Caspersson, T. and Hydén, H., "Högrevirusarters förökning." *Nord. Med.* 28:2631. (English translation in Cold Spring Harbor Symp. XII, 104, 1947.)

1945, 9   Moberger (unpublished).

1946, 1   Caspersson, T. and Engström, A., "The transparency of the corneal tissue." *Nord. Med.* 30:1277.

1946, 2   Wilton, Å. and Thorell, B., "Dentincellernas nukleotidomsättning under normala förhållanden och vid C-vitamin-brist." *Nord. Med.* 31:1784.

1946,   3   Engström, A., "Quantitative micro- and histochemical elementary analysis by roentgen absorption spectrography." *Acta Radiol.* Suppl. LXIII.

1946,   4   Engström, A., "Quantitative microchemical and histochemical analysis of elements by X-rays." *Nature* 158:664.

1947,   1   Caspersson, T., "The relations between nucleic acid and protein synthesis." *Symp. Soc. Exp. Biol.* 1:127.

1947,   2   Engström, A., "Qualitative microchemical analysis by microradiography with fluorescent screen." *Experientia* 3:208.

1947,   3   Engström, A. and Lindström, B., "Histochemical analysis by X-rays of long wave lengths." *Experientia* 3:191.

1947,   4   Engström, A. and Lindström, B., "Quantitative cytochemical determination of nitrogen by X-ray absorption spectrography." *Biochim. et Biophys. Acta* 1:428.

1947,   5   Engström, A. and Lindström, B., "New differential X-ray absorption method for elementary chemical analysis." *Rev. Sci. Instruments* 18:681.

1947,   6   Hamberger, C.-A. and Hydén, H., "Alteraciones en el Cido Interno Después de Estimulacion Acústica." *El Dia Medico* XIX.

1947,   7   Hamberger, C.-A. and Hydén, H., "Cytochemical studies on experimental bone fistulae." *Acta Oto-Laryngol.* 35:479.

1947,   8   Hydén, H., "Protein and nucleotide metabolism in the nerve cell under different functional conditions." *Symposia of the Soc. for Exp. Biol.* 1:150.

1947,   9   Malmgren, B. and Hedén, C.-G., "Nucleotide metabolism of bacteria and the bacterial nucleus." *Nature* 159:577.

1947, 10   Malmgren, B. and Hedén, C.-G., "Some aspects of the nucleotide metabolism and variations of volume in bacteria." *Proc. VI Intern. Congr. Cytol.*

1947, 11   Malmgren, B. and Hedén, C.-G., "New results concerning the nucleotide metabolism of bacteria." *Proc. VI Intern. Congr. Microbiol.*

1947, 12   Malmgren, B. and Hedén, C.-G., "Studies of the nucleotide metabolism of bacteria. I. Ultraviolet microspectrography as an aid in the study of the nucleotide content of bacteria." *Acta Path. Microbiol. Scand.* 24:417.

1947, 13   Malmgren, B. and Hedén, C.-G., "Studies of the nucleotide metabolism of bacteria. II. Aspects of the problem of the bacterial nucleus." *Acta Path. Microbiol. Scand.* 24:437.

1947, 14   Malmgren, B. and Hedén, C.-G., "Studies of the nucleotide metabolism of bacteria. III. The nucleotide metabolism of the gramnegative bacteria." *Acta Path. Microbiol. Scand.* 24:448.

1947, 15   Malmgren, B. and Hedén, C.-G., "Studies of the nucleotide metabolism of bacteria. IV. The nucleotide metabolism of the grampositive bacteria." *Acta Path. Microbiol. Scand.* 24:472.

1947, 16   Malmgren, B. and Hedén, C-G., "Studies of the nucleotide metabolism of bacteria. V. Volume variations and nucleotide metabolism in Protein Vulgaris." *Acta Path. Microbiol. Scand.* 24:496.

1947, 17   Thorell, B., "Studies on the formation of cellular substances during blood cell production." *Acta Med. Scand.* Suppl. CC.

1947, 18   Thorell, B., "The connection between hemoglobin synthesis and growth during blood cell formation." *Proc. VI Intern. Congr. Cytol.*

1947, 19   Thorell, B., "The relation of nucleic acids to the formation and differentiation of cellular proteins." *Symposium on Quant. Biol. XII,* Cold Spring Harbor.

1947, 20   Stowell, R. (under publication)

1948, 1   Bauer, H. and Caspersson, T., "Cytochemical observations on nucleolus formation in Chironomus." *Proc. VIII Intern. Congr. Genet.,* p. 533.

1948, 2   Engström, A. and Jakus, M. A., "Intracellular determination of protein by X-ray microspectrography." *Nature* 161:168.

1948, 3   Hydén, H., and Hartelius, H., "Stimulation of the nucleoprotein-production in the nerve cells by malononitrile and its effect on psychic functions in mental disorders." *Acta Psychiat. et Neurol.* Suppl. XLVIII.

1948, 4   Thorell, B., "Behaviour of the nucleolus-associated chromatin during cell maturation." *Proc. VIII Intern. Congr. Genet.*

1948, 5   Thorell, B., "The relation of the synthesis of hemoglobin to the cellular growth during normal and certain pathological conditions." *Acta Path. Microbiol. Scand.* 25:54.

1948, 6 Thorell, B., "Cytochemical aspects on growth and differentiation during blood cell formation." *Proc. I Intern. Congr. Hematol.*

1948, 7 Thorson (under publication).

1948, 8 Caspersson, T., "The nucleus in normal and pathological cells." In *Acidi Nucleici* . . . , Torino, 1948.

1948, 9 Schultz, J. and Caspersson, T., "Nucleic acids in Drosophila eggs and Y-chromosome effects." *Nature* 163:66.

1948, 10 Stowell, R., "Nucleic acids and cytologic changes in regenerating rat liver." *Arch. Path.* 46:164.

THE THOMAS WILLIAM SALMON
MEMORIAL LECTURES

The Salmon Lectures of the New York Academy of Medicine were established in 1931, as a memorial to Thomas William Salmon, M.D., and for the advancement of the objects to which his professional career had been wholly devoted.

Dr. Salmon died in 1927, at the age of 51, after a career of extraordinary service in psychiatric practice and education, and in the development of a world-wide movement for the better treatment and prevention of mental disorders, and for the promotion of mental health.

Following his death, a group of his many friends organized a committee for the purpose of establishing one or more memorials that might serve to preserve and pass on to future generations some of the spirit and purpose of his supremely noble and useful life. Five hundred and ninety-six subscriptions were received, three hundred and nineteen from physicians.

Of the amount thus obtained, $100,000 was, on January 10, 1931, given to the New York Academy of Medicine, as a fund to provide an income for the support of an annual series of lectures and for other projects for the advancement of psychiatry and mental hygiene. For the purpose of giving lasting quality to the lectures as a memorial to Dr. Salmon, and of extending their usefulness, it was stipulated that each series should be published in a bound volume of which this volume is one.

Lectures Published in This Series